RE-ENGINEERING THE MANUFACTURING SYSTEM

MANUFACTURING ENGINEERING AND MATERIALS PROCESSING
A Series of Reference Books and Textbooks

FOUNDING EDITOR

Geoffrey Boothroyd
University of Rhode Island
Kingston, Rhode Island

RE-ENGINEERING THE MANUFACTURING SYSTEM

APPLYING THE THEORY OF CONSTRAINTS

ROBERT E. STEIN
Consultant
Cedar Park, Texas

Marcel Dekker, Inc.   New York • Basel • Hong Kong

Stein, Robert E.
  Re-engineering the manufacturing system: applying the theory of
constraints / Robert E. Stein.
      p.   cm.—(Manufacturing engineering and materials processing; 47)
      Includes bibliographical references and index.
      ISBN 0-8247-9747-7 (alk. paper)
      1. Production management. 2. Reengineering (Management) 3. Com-
puter integrated manufacturing systems. I. Title. II. Series.
  TS155.S769   1996
  658.5—dc20   96–18120
                                                                  CIP

The publisher offers discounts on this book when ordered in bulk quantities. For
more information, write to Special Sales/Professional Marketing at the address
below.

This book is printed on acid-free paper.

MARCEL DEKKER, INC.
270 Madison Avenue, New York, New York 10016

Current printing (last digit):
10 9 8 7 6 5 4 3 2 1

PRINTED IN THE UNITED STATES OF AMERICA

To my wife, Debera, for her love and support;
to my daughters, Jennifer and Allyson, and to my granddaughter, Jessica

Foreword

With the publication of *Re-Engineering the Manufacturing System: Applying the Theory of Constraints*, Bob Stein has made an important contribution to the manufacturing systems portion of the emerging Theory of Constraints (TOC) literature. The book provides answers to two very basic and important questions in today's systems marketplace:

> What should be re-engineered?
> Answer: The infrastructure of manufacturing information systems.

> What should it be re-engineered *to*?
> Answer: To the public domain specification for integrated manufacturing decision support, shop control and scheduling systems described in the book *The Haystack Syndrome*.

Bob is in an excellent position to write a book on this subject. With over 20 years of experience, he has led MRP implementations in large accounts throughout the world. His background in TOC includes attending the Avraham Y. Goldratt Institute's two-week TOC "Jonah" course and participating in the so-called second wave of the institute's Certified Information Systems Associate (CISA) program. Created by TOC systems pioneer, Avraham Mordoch, the CISA program provided education and consulting support for the trailblazing manufacturing companies that participated as development partners with the institute. This period of conceptual development and field testing gave rise to the subject of this book, the public domain TOC manufacturing decision support, shop control and scheduling specification described in *The Haystack Syndrome*. As a member of the American Production and Inventory Control

Society (APICS) Constraints Management Special Interest Group (CM SIG), Bob has served as subcommittee chairman for "TOC and Total Quality" issues and courses. He is featured in the 1996 APICS National Workshops program as the developer and instructor for the course "TOC and Total Quality." That course arose out of Bob's timely and generous response to the CM SIG's request for donated APICS-owned TOC courseware and is based on his first book, *The Next Phase of Total Quality Management: TQM II and the Focus on Profitability* (Marcel Dekker, 1993). Currently, Bob is leading the CM SIG committee's efforts to formulate strategies concerning APICS TOC courseware and certifications in the area of TOC manufacturing systems.

TOC is a physics. It seeks to uncover the underlying nature of things. TOC's applications to the manufacturing industries are introduced in many publications, but primarily *The Goal* (1984, with a major and important 1992 revision), *The Haystack Syndrome: Sifting Information from the Data Ocean* (1990) and *It's Not Luck* (1994). *The Goal* and *It's Not Luck* are business texts written in the form of novels. Taken together, they have sold in the millions around the world in several languages. They are by far the most friendly and effective introductions to TOC and its major principles. The role of *The Haystack Syndrome* in the TOC literature is to define the generic solution for integrated manufacturing decision support, shop control and finite capacity production scheduling. It asserts the need to replace traditional cost accounting for manufacturing business decisions, proceeds to develop the solution and creates related specifications for shop control and scheduling along the way. The author of all three of these books is physicist and educator Dr. Eliyahu M. Goldratt, the founder of the Avraham Y. Goldratt Institute in New Haven, Connecticut, and the originator of the Theory of Constraints.

In the current volume, Bob Stein extends the *Haystack Syndrome* analysis in three important ways. First, he addresses several key shortcomings of existing systems, and several important aspects of the TOC solution, at greater levels of detail. For example, this book offers a more detailed look at the many *workcenter-level* "scheduling" tools available within traditional shop floor control systems and explains why there is simply no way they can perform as well as TOC's *company-level* drum-buffer-rope and dynamic buffering solutions. Not that the old system is bad; the traditional tools are in widespread use today and are helpful to many people in their daily work. However, Bob helps readers see that the TOC tools will allow those same manufacturing people to accomplish more on a larger scale with less effort from their daily "scheduling" activities. Second, he extends the *Haystack* analysis by tailoring the scope, terminology and graphics to match what the manufacturing systems community normally sees in their textbooks. Finally, issues of data structure and implementation are addressed. These include changes to performance measurements, use of TOC thinking processes for dealing with policy constraints and other matters which were either outside the intended scope of *The Haystack Syndrome* or were invented since its publication.

These contributions make *Re-Engineering the Manufacturing System* an especially helpful volume for manufacturing systems managers, practitioners, consultants, designers and programmers seeking additional and timely information about the emerging TOC systems standards. Like his previous book on TOC and TQM, this text will assist many disparate constituencies in taking important initial steps toward understanding, consensus and cooperation.

Thomas B. McMullen, Jr.
Founding Chairman, APICS Constraints Management
Special Interest Group (CM SIG)
Weston, Massachusetts

Preface

Originally designed by software engineers to fit the computer environment, traditional manufacturing system concepts are now over 30 years old. In that time tremendous changes have occurred in hardware and software, but little has changed in the basic design concepts. The processes of master production scheduling and gross to net requirements generation are the same now as when first conceived. Little progress has been made to really improve the majority of systems being marketed today. Recent trends that increase the rate at which planning occurs to simulate scheduling or materials planning scenarios have merely created the opportunity for users to do the wrong things faster.

The traditional closed-loop systems were not designed by examining the cause and effect relationships within the environments in which they were to function or by developing cold, hard facts about how resources are related to one another. Had the original systems been based on a thorough understanding of the physical requirements rather than by looking first at what the computer could do, a totally different system would exist today. It would be a system that was fully grounded in reality. It is only when the problem has been sufficiently defined that a system can be created which will truly solve the problem.

In 1990 Dr. Eliyahu M. Goldratt presented an outline of such a system in his book *The Haystack Syndrome.* Also included were a measurement system and the thought processes behind why the system must work as it does. In recent years the "Haystack Compatible" system has been growing in acceptance and has even been promoted by the recently established Constraints Management Special Interest Group (CM SIG) of the American Production and Inventory Control Society. This is an important change. Hopefully it means that the old

MRP-based systems are going to be replaced by ones that discriminate between data and information.

If the decision process is to change to the extent advocated in *The Haystack Syndrome* and *The Next Phase of Total Quality Management*, then it is time to take a serious look at making some changes in the information system—not superficial changes like adding additional reporting functionality, but major ones. This book is a detailed instruction guide on how to build, implement and use a manufacturing system based on the Theory of Constraints (TOC). I hope to give enough information so that manufacturing software companies can begin the process of modifying the traditional system to better conform to reality and to help those faced with the job of implementing a TOC-based system to better understand what they are attempting to do.

I would like to offer my thanks to some special people. Without their education, patience and dedication to a worthy cause, this book would not have been possible. Thank you, Dr. Eli Goldratt, Avraham Mordoch, Eli Schragenheim and the staff and former associates of the Goldratt Institute. I would also like to thank Tom McMullen, the original Certified Information Systems Associate.

Robert E. Stein

Contents

RE-ENGINEERING THE MANUFACTURING SYSTEM

1

An Introduction

This chapter offers a brief history of the manufacturing information system, introduces the possibility that an improved methodology is available and lays the groundwork for what is to follow.

CHAPTER OBJECTIVES

- To provide an overview for this book
- To lay a historical foundation

THE ADVENT OF THE TRADITIONAL SYSTEM

In 1974 Joseph Orlicky documented in his book *Material Requirements Planning* what had become one of the biggest changes to American manufacturing since the Industrial Revolution. Orlicky presented in intricate detail the design, interface and calculation issues for what was called the manufacturing information system.

The advent of the computer and its ability to store and manipulate large volumes of data made it possible to create demand for upper level finished goods items, drive demand for lower level assemblies and raw material parts and schedule the shop floor. For an industry that had been planning every part based on individual usage rates this was a major step forward.

While he was not alone in this change, his book would become one of the most read in the American Production and Inventory Control Society (APICS) library for years to come. Oliver Wight and others, pioneers in the field, had also begun this documentation process. Each had been involved for some time in the creation of these systems. During the late 1960s and early 1970s, as these systems became reality, companies would see an opportunity to mainstream the computer system into American business. By the end of the 1970s and early 1980s the processes of master production scheduling, material requirements planning, capacity requirements planning and shop floor control became commonplace. The closed loop system (Figure 1.1) became the most recognized graphic of the manufacturing systems industry.

The accepted technology had become so ingrained in industry, software companies and consulting organizations as well as at the university level that it soon became very difficult to make any significant changes. Those changes that did occur were simply built on top of the assumptions upon which the original systems were designed.

Hampering any efforts to create improvements in the technology were the millions of dollars invested to create the software that would run this nation's economy. Once written, manufacturing systems became not just software, but an investment which had to be protected by those who wrote or bought them. And, once learned by the user, this knowledge became job security. The slowness of the acceptance of techniques like Just-In-Time or the Theory of Constraints is

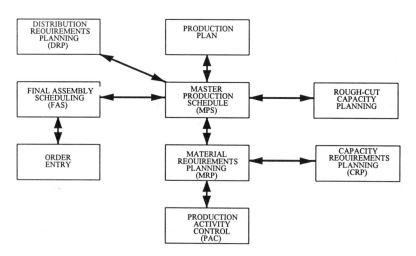

Figure 1.1 The closed loop system.

evidence of the difficulties which had to be overcome in implementing new methodologies. Possibly the greatest problem to overcome can be summed up in a statement uttered by the head of manufacturing consulting for a major U.S. corporation, "It doesn't matter whether you're right or wrong this is what General Motors wants." There is a tremendous amount of money to be made in the consulting industry in this country. For the benefit of the uninitiated it must be understood that being right isn't necessarily the goal.

It was never a secret that there might be problems with the technology. In Orlicky's book, now 20 years old, pages 46-48 provide some insight into the conflicts which existed at the time and are made very clear. Material requirements planning (MRP) was known to be "capacity insensitive." However, the benefits so far outweighed the problems inherent in the order launch and expedite system commonly known as EOQ-ROP, or economic order quantity and re-order point, that the problems were ignored. At least for a while. The advent of finite capacity planning seemingly made it possible to now synchronize the way in which raw material was ordered with the way it was to be consumed by the resources and the market. Unfortunately the problems involved in attempting to accomplish this task were based upon the assumptions of the original system, making it virtually impossible to do effectively.

Two issues which greatly hampered the creation of an effective system were cost accounting and a complete lack of knowledge of the physical laws which govern the manufacturing environment. The objective of the original system was to use the computers calculating abilities to time phase material requirements. However, to do this correctly meant that the system must resemble reality. And this is where things were done, which made today's manufacturing systems much less effective than they could be.

EXPLORING A DIFFERENT APPROACH

In the mid- to late 1970s Dr. Eli Goldratt, with a background in physics, approached the information system from a totally different perspective. His observations, unfettered by the traditional thought process, resulted in his solving some very interesting problems and creating a technology which has proved to be far superior to the traditional manufacturing system. In his books *The Goal* (1992), *The Race* (1986) and *The Haystack Syndrome* (1990) and in classes at the Goldratt Institute, Dr. Goldratt presented a totally new way of looking at information as being the answer to the question asked. While this seems a trivial issue and is just common sense, if you get the question wrong or do not know how to answer it, you cannot begin to build the information system. This is where the fun begins. The questions as well as the answers are totally different than what has been taught for the last 50 years. With this in mind, how can anyone be expected to build the information system?

Providing the Key

It is very clear that a manufacturing system is not just a tool for planning material and scheduling the factory. It is an integral part of the five steps of improvement for the "throughput environment" as defined in *The Haystack Syndrome* and in *The Next Phase of Total Quality Management* (1993). The key issue which defines the effectiveness of the information system is how well it supports the TOC principles of

- Identifying the constraint
- Exploiting the constraint
- Subordinating the remaining resources
- Elevating the constraint
- Repeating the process

It is this sequence of steps which literally defines what an information system must do. Following them to their logical conclusions means that a system must aid in the identification, exploitation and elevation of the constraint and with the subordination of the remaining resources. For this to occur means that the logic of the system must be very different than it is in the traditional system.

In *The Haystack Syndrome*, Dr. Goldratt also defines the structure of the information system. He establishes three separate segments along with justification for each. These segments include

- What if
- Control
- Schedule

His objective was to create a system which can help in answering questions, or to play the "what if" game. To support the "what if" there must be a "schedule" so that the physical laws governing the process can be addressed, and there must be a "control" so that problems which may arise can be addressed before they impact the schedule. This whole concept will be addressed in Chapter 3.

AN OVERVIEW OF THIS BOOK

The remaining chapters of this book are dedicated to presenting the problems associated with the traditional system's ability to support the five steps and to present, in detail, those solutions provided by the Theory of Constraints. The objective is to provide enough background as well as detailed information to allow industry to begin the process of re-defining the information system.

It represents a tremendous change in the distinction of what an information system is and what it should do and lays the groundwork for the design of the next generation of systems, including:

- Design
- Focusing mechanisms
- Processing logic
- Structure

The objective here is not to eliminate the MRP II system but to change it so that it will be more in line with the goal of the company. MRP II has created a great data system upon which to draw. How to use these data to implement the five steps is another issue. There must be a change.

Organization

- Chapter 2—"Visiting the Traditional System"—is a general overview of the problems associated with the traditional manufacturing system. The traditional system presents some very serious problems which must be overcome before it can really be called an information system.
- Chapter 3—"Establishing the Characteristics of an Information System"—addresses, from a conceptual perspective, what an information system should do and how it should be organized. This is the first step in building a system which is based on reality.
- Chapter 4—"Defining the Structure"—provides a global view of how the information system is structured. It puts every segment of the system into place and defines the interfaces between the various processes, including input and output.
- Chapter 5—"Identifying the Constraint"—deals with the intricate details of how the system identifies the constraint, including processing logic.

- Chapter 6—"Exploitation." It is not enough to identify the constraint. It governs the amount of money a company can make. It must be exploited for every dollar, yen or pound that can be gained. Chapter 6 presents the processing logic for the exploitation phase.
- Chapter 7—"Subordination." Once the constraint has been exploited, all the remaining resources must give the constraint what it needs and nothing more. Chapter 7 details the subordination logic.
- Chapter 8—"Buffer Management." The system must be protected from those things which can and will go wrong. Chapter 8 presents the logic of the buffering process and buffer management.
- Chapter 9—"Supporting the Decision Process." Once a complete definition of an information system has been made, how then should it be used to maximize the creation of throughput? By aiding in the process of answering specific questions, such as what lot size should be used, should a certain product be obtained from internal or external resources, and what price should I accept for a given product, the system can provide information that will make a difference
- Chapter 10—"Making Strategic Decisions." How and where a company should grow is important. One of the most significant uses of the information system is in setting the strategic direction. Chapter 10 presents how the system should be used to segment markets, plan corporate growth, plan long-term efforts and recession-proof the company.
- Chapter 11—"Modifying the Current System"—addresses the issues associated with how to modify the current system to conform to reality. It answers the questions of what should be eliminated and what should be kept. Throwing out the traditional system is not the answer. The current information system can provide a tremendous platform on which to build. What should be kept and what should be eliminated are major questions that need to be addressed.
- Chapter 12—"Implementation." When the design of the system is shifted to the extent that is being addressed here the old methods often can cause problems. Implementing a different kind of system can mean using a different approach. Chapter 12 addresses those changes which must be made in how the new information system is implemented to be successful.

SUMMARY

Re-engineering the traditional system presents some interesting opportunities for improving the profitability of many companies. While it is not the only issue which must be addressed, it can make a major difference not only in scheduling the factory but in helping to eliminate many managerial, behavioral, logistical or policy constraints which limit the company's ability to "make more money now as well as in the future." The technology is available. It is time to realize that a change can and should be made. The sooner, the better.

STUDY QUESTIONS

1. What was the impact that the traditional information system had on manufacturing companies in the United States, and what benefit(s) does it provide?

2. According to the theory of constraints what process must be imbedded in the logic of a successful information system.

3. What is the definition of information?

4. Describe the traditional closed loop system and provide a diagram indicating the order in which individual modules should appear.

5. What is the basic structure of the information system?

2

Visiting the Traditional System

The basic problem associated with the traditional system, whether infinite or finite capacity, is that the processing logic used makes it virtually impossible to successfully implement the five steps of improvement. The user is unable to identify or exploit the constraint and to subordinate the remaining resources. It was just not designed for this purpose and yet this is what must be done. (see *The Haystack Syndrome*, 1990, or *The Next Phase of Total Quality Management*, 1993).

CHAPTER OBJECTIVES

- To address the problems associated with the traditional MRP II system, including rough-cut capacity planning, material requirements planning, capacity requirements planning and shop floor control
- To begin the process of understanding the problems that the new generation of systems must solve

THE ASSUMPTIONS OF THE TRADITIONAL SYSTEM

The processing logic of the traditional system makes some very large assumptions which reality will not ignore. Those assumptions include but are not limited to the following topics:

- Relationships between resources
- Static versus dynamic data
- The aggregation of demand
- Statistical fluctuations

Relationships Between Resources

Because resources are not just isolated islands of production but interact regularly, they will have specific influences over each other based on where they are in the process and their physical characteristics. These influences must be reproduced in the system. The information system must be a simulation of reality. Without this quality, the information system is merely a data system.

Static Versus Dynamic Data

Hampering any ability to simulate reality within the company is the way in which certain data are used. Data which should be dynamic in nature are instead stored as static and recalled from the data base without consideration of the changes which may have occurred or the physical laws which govern how it should be used.

The Aggregation of Demand

During the process of assessing available capacity and comparing it to demand, the tendency is to aggregate both into time buckets. This process overlooks one very important issue. It assumes that all the time in a given time bucket is available for all orders in the bucket. Unfortunately this is not a valid assumption and is a major issue with regard to how the traditional system manages capacity.

Statistical Fluctuations

In manufacturing, as in nature, all things will vary. This is a basic law. No two items are produced exactly alike. They will always be different. Similarly, manufacturing resources will always fluctuate in their ability to produce. Sometimes they will produce more than average. Other times they will produce less. The methodology for handling this in the typical manufacturing system is to build in buffers between each resource. It is not only how these buffers are built which raises some interesting questions, but how the instructions for executing the production plan cause problems by providing data which will sabotage the entire scheduling process.

Note: since each of these issues applies throughout the system, the approach used will be to describe the traditional system and then apply the assumption involved with the above topics. The most logical place to begin is with the master production schedule.

MASTER PRODUCTION SCHEDULING

The objective of the master production schedule (MPS) is to provide input to the system for those requirements currently needed by the customer (sales orders) or those which have been predicted to be needed in the future (forecast). It is significant in that it is what drives the remaining processes within MRP II (see Figure 2.1).

From the master schedule, requirements are driven into material requirements planning (MRP) so that the quantity of specific components, lot sizes and their time phasing can be accomplished. From MRP action messages are created to launch purchase orders for parts which must be obtained from outside the company and to launch work orders for those items to be built inside the

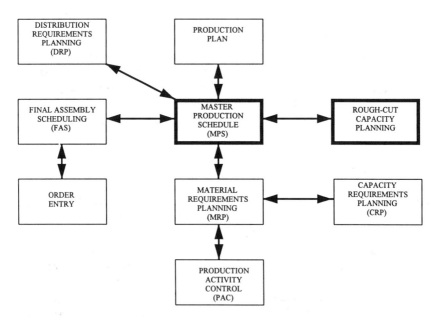

Figure 2.1 The closed loop system—master production schedule.

company. Using the input of the MPS, MRP becomes the guiding factor in creating the schedule for the entire facility.

Given this information, it is obvious that to be successful in creating a valid master production schedule the ability of the system to produce according to demand requires that the capability of the system be known. The traditional method for the process of understanding the capability of the system prior to attempting to create the MPS is called rough-cut capacity planning (RCCP).

Rough-Cut Capacity Planning

To provide the ability to perform rough-cut capacity planning many systems will store a profile of how certain products are produced. Included in the profile is the related load to be placed on specific resources during the manufacturing process.

Figure 2.2 represents a specific routing or load requirement to produce one part AFG. Stored for each resource, R-1 through R-4, is the time required for each step (Figure 2.2). Notice that it takes three hours on resource R-1 to produce one AFG. These data when combined with demand from the MPS and similar data

Part: AFG - Planned Routing	
Work Center	Time/ Part
R-1	3.0
R-2	5.0
R-3	2.0
R-4	4.0

Figure 2.2 The product profile.

Part: AFG	1	2	3	4	5	6
Requirement				10		

Figure 2.3   Establishing demand with rough-cut capacity planning—10 parts shown in period 4.

for other parts on the master schedule will create a total demand and percent load figure for all resources in the process. Figure 2.3 presents demand for 10 AFGs in period 4 originating from the master schedule.

This demand is multiplied by the individual resource time to produce the part (see Figure 2.4). The demand for 10 part AFGs in period 4 of the MPS created a load of 30 hours on resource R-1. When combined with the demand for DEF and XYZ the total demand for R-1 is 140 hours, or a 117% load.

Work Center	PRODUCT			Capacity	Demand	Load %
	AFG	DEF	XYZ	Capacity	Demand	Load %
R-1	30	50	60	120	140	117
R-2	50	20	30	100	100	100
R-3	20	30	20	130	70	53
R-4	40	40	10	120	90	75

Figure 2.4   Rough-cut capacity planning example data.

Time Phasing the Rough-Cut Capacity Plan

Some systems will take one extra step and attempt to time phase by storing relative lead time with the load data for each resource.

Figure 2.5 presents five operations each being processed on different resources. It also shows setup and run times as well as the relative period to load the demand for each resource. When the additional lead time data is added it facilitates placing each operation in relative time with the next. Notice that operations 10 and 20 fall into period 1 while operations 30 and 40 fall into period 2. After being extended by the quantity and due date for the individual product on the MPS, the load requirements for setup and run time can be placed in a relative position in time (see Figure 2.6).

The 10 parts required from the MPS for period 4 have been converted to labor requirements and placed in time for each of the resources in the load profile. Note that the labor for the saw and lathe appear in period 2, the first day of processing. Mill and heat treat were placed in the second day of processing. The load for the inspection operation appears in period 4, the last day of processing.

Addressing the Problems

Even when lead time is added the data created in no way resemble reality. It is a gross distortion to assume that all time within a given time block is equally available to each order.

LOAD PROFILE				
OPER.	WORK CENTER	SETUP TIME	RUN TIME	PERIOD
10	SAW	.15	.50	1
20	LATHE	.50	1.50	1
30	MILL	.30	1.30	2
40	HEAT TREAT	.50	1.50	2
50	INSPECT	.15	.50	3

Figure 2.5   Time phasing the load profile.

Master Schedule

Part: A	1	2	3	4	5	6
Requirement				10		

Load Requirements

W/C	1	2	3	4	5	6
Saw		5.15				
Lathe		15.50				
Mill			13.30			
Heat Treat			15.50			
Inspect				5.15		

Figure 2.6   Time phasing rough-cut capacity planning.

Figure 2.7 shows a capacity plan with a level load for five periods. From this illustration it is apparent that this resource has no real capacity problems. However, this is an oversimplification of what really happens as orders are placed in time.

The objective of capacity planning is to understand the impact of a specific load on the system's ability to deliver to the customer. Aggregation of demand into time blocks as in Figure 2.7 hides the fact that each order is placed in a specific location in time with individual start and stop dates, and this placement has certain implications.

Figure 2.8 shows five orders, **A** through **E**, on a single resource and is a more realistic view of how orders are scheduled across a resource and why the aggregation of demand causes problems.

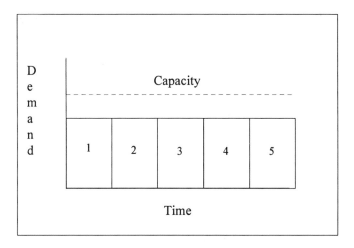

Figure 2.7 The aggregation of demand.

Each order is placed in time so that it has adequate protection and will arrive at shipping by a specific scheduled due date. By aggregating demand the assumption is made that the time to the right of order D is as equally available as the time to the left. However, the time to the right exists to protect the delivery to

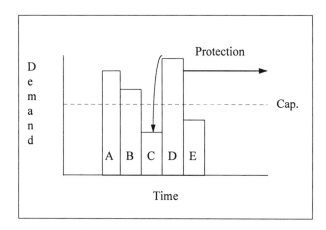

Figure 2.8 Offsetting for protection.

shipping on time. If any of the load for D is moved to the right the sales order due date will be immediately invalidated. The only additional time available to process order D is to the left. But, under rough-cut capacity planning all time is considered equally available within the same time block. This is a serious problem.

Aggregating demand to a given time bucket is like putting one hand in boiling water and the other in a block of ice and feeling OK because on average you're at 98.6 degrees Fahrenheit. Unfortunately, a rough-cut is not good enough to be able to set the master production schedule. This means that the initial estimation of material requirements based on the input of the master production schedule would have no basis in reality. It is simply a wish list.

Since rough-cut capacity planning has failed to provide adequate capacity information, the hope at this point would be to set a preliminary master schedule, input that data to material requirements planning and then check to see if capacity is available through capacity requirements planning (CRP). Unfortunately, the logic of MRP and CRP also present major problems in accomplishing this task.

MATERIAL REQUIREMENTS PLANNING

Material requirements planning has been called the "engine" that makes the manufacturing system work. It takes output from the master production schedule and:

- Determines the parts requirements for lower level assemblies and raw material
- Manages the timing of planned and scheduled work orders and purchase orders
- Notifies the materials planner when to launch new orders or reschedule old ones
- Drives the capacity requirements planning and shop floor control systems

Because of its position in the overall manufacturing system it is an extremely important process. However, it is also one which has some very serious problems (see Figure 2.9).

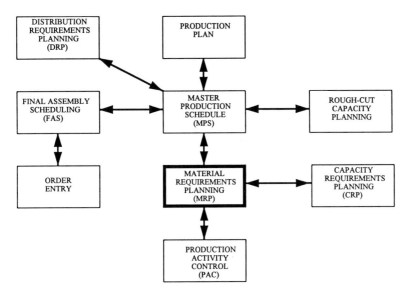

Figure 2.9 The closed loop system (material requirements planning).

Dynamic Versus Static Data in MRP

For an information system to resemble reality it must be dynamic in nature. While MRP II systems are dynamic and are able to change as the situation changes with respect to issues such as the planning of material requirements, in general they do not have the kind of dynamics required to recreate and react to those physical laws which govern the environment in which they operate. This issue alone makes it impossible to use MRP in executing the five steps of improvement. As an example, certain items of data such as lead times are stored in the item master as static and yet lead times should grow and contract as the dynamics of the situation dictate. In the gross to net requirements matrix shown in Figure 2.10 there are gross requirements of 10 As due in period 6.

There are no scheduled receipts or on-hand quantities to offset the need. So, net requirements of 10 As are generated for the same period. Since the lot size to be used is lot for lot, as seen in the item master data at the bottom of the figure, 10 As are planned to fill the net requirement. The lead time from the item master is used to determine the release date of the order. The quantity of 10 As to be received in period 6 generated a planned order for 10 As to be released in period 4. In this case, MRP assumed that both the lead time and the lot size were static and would not change.

	1	2	3	4	5	6
GROSS REQMTS.						10
SCHED. REC.						
PLAN O/H						
NET REQMNTS.						10
PLAN REC.						10
PLAN REL.				10		
LEAD TIME = 2 LOT SIZE = L4L						

Figure 2.10   Gross to net requirements generation.

An issue can be made that most systems use the concept of fixed and variable lead time to solve this problem. As illustrated in Figure 2.11, the planned receipt was doubled resulting in a corresponding increase in lead time. The original order planned for period four is now due in period 2.

This issue serves to illustrate the lack of understanding on the part of MRP developers. The key question which must be answered is what generates the need for a specific lead time? To understand this also means understanding what causes lead times to fluctuate. It is possible for two significantly different lot sizes under similar circumstances to have no difference in lead time requirements. Why? It is also possible for the same lot size under different circumstances to have a large difference in lead time requirements. Why?

To answer these questions requires a better understanding of capacity. As seen in *The Haystack Syndrome* and in *The Next Phase of Total Quality Management*, there are three types:

- Productive—the capacity required to produce a product.
- Protective—the capacity required to offset for those things which can go wrong.
- Excess—the capacity which is over the amount of productive and protective capacity required

	1	2	3	4	5	6
GROSS REQMTS.						20
SCHED. REC.						
PLAN O/H						
NET REQMNTS.						20
PLAN REC.						20
PLAN REL.		20				

LEAD TIME = 2
LOT SIZE = L4L
LEAD TIME = Variable

Figure 2.11 Variable lead time.

It is the fluctuation in the protective capacity available which determines lead time. Figure 2.12 illustrates this.

As the load on a given resource increases, the amount of capacity available to use in the protection of the constraint actually decreases. At a seventy percent load, resources A, B and C have enough capacity to ensure that resource D (the constraint) is protected from any delays which might occur. However, if the load on resource C were to be increased to 90%, the amount of capacity available to protect the constraint would decrease. In other words, there would

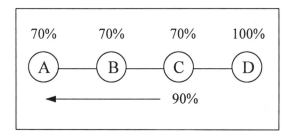

Figure 2.12 Fluctuation in protective capacity.

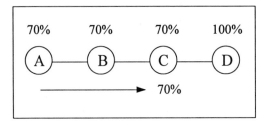

Figure 2.13   Fluctuation in protective capacity.

not be enough capacity left at resource C to ensure that if something were to delay production for any reason orders would still reach D on time. To ensure that inventory reaches the constraint without excessive delay raw material must be released earlier, thus creating an increase in lead time.

As the load decreases and the available protective capacity increases, the impact of fluctuations in the productive capability have less of an impact so that material can be released later, thus causing lead times to shrink (see Figure 2.13).

When resource C's load is returned to seventy percent the amount of protection for D is increased and raw material can be released later. This means that in order to accomplish the process of offsetting for lead time there must be some estimation of the amount of protection required while running the material requirement process. This is a different situation than what is being answered by the rough-cut or capacity requirements planning process.

As illustrated in Figure 2.10, gross to net requirements generation considers lead time as static. In Figure 2.11 it assumes that an increase in lot size would automatically increase the load and therefore increases lead time without ever looking at the impact on protective capacity. Even though the lead time seemed dynamic in the second example, it was really just a multiple of static data stored in the item master and had no basis in reality.

The Cascading Effect

The problems associated with static data are exacerbated when it is considered that each part within each level of the bill of material is treated in the same fashion (see Figure 2.14).

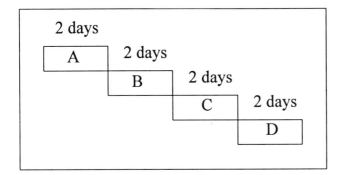

Figure 2.14 The cascading effect.

In gross to net requirements generation, the planned release of the parent becomes the gross requirement of the child, and the netting process continues at the child level. The item master is once again consulted for lead time and lot sizing information. Notice that the end item, product A, has a two-day lead time. Part B's requirements are created to fill parts requirements for an order of As. But part B must be available in its entirety to fill A's material requirements at the start of the order. This means that regardless of the reality of what might be occurring on the shop floor or what might be necessary to compress lead time, MRP ignores it.

In Figure 2.14 MRP has already assumed that the lead time to create product A is 8 days by simply adding all of the static lead times in the process. Anyone who has ever implemented an MRP system has run into problems resulting from this issue. Lead times are exaggerated and inventory goes up.

Additionally, material requirements planning assumes that the process batch size and transfer batch size will remain the same throughout the process. It does not plan for overlapping operations. If the best method for reducing lead time is to transfer in batches of one, then MRP must plan its work orders in batches of one—not a good idea.

The Use of Lot Sizing Algorithms

Most MRP systems have a number of lot sizing methods used to sub-optimize between the cost of setup and the cost of carrying inventory. Various methods include but are not limited to:

- Economic order quantity
- Part period balancing
- Period order quantity
- Least unit cost
- Least total cost

For these methods the thought process is that the higher the number of setups the greater the setup cost. Conversely, the larger the lot size the larger the carrying cost. Supposedly there is a balancing point where the minimum total cost can be determined by choosing a lot size which sub-optimizes the setup and inventory carrying cost. If the lot size is any larger or smaller than the economic order quantity then total cost will be driven upward.

Economic Order Quantity

The economic order quantity (EOQ) formula is stated as follows:

$$\sqrt{\frac{2US}{IC}}$$

where U = Annual usage
       S = Setup cost
       I = Inventory carrying cost
       C = Unit cost

The EOQ formula is represented graphically in Figure 2.15.

Line AB represents the declining setup cost as the lot size becomes larger and fewer setups are actually made. Line CD represents the rising carrying cost associated with having to carry more inventory for a longer period of time. Where the two lines meet is the point at which the total cost is the lowest. The lot size of 50 would require that 5 setups be made to fill an order for 250 parts. A lot size of 250 would only have one setup.

The concept of the economic order quantity makes some very questionable assumptions. If any one of these assumptions are broken, the entire economic order lot sizing process would be invalidated, including all those previously listed. Those assumptions made are that

1. Each setup activity will result in a cost since activity absorbs labor dollars.

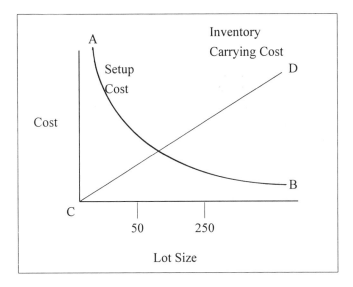

Figure 2.15 Economic order quantity.

2. Setup costs will remain constant.
3. A given lot size will remain constant.
4. Carrying cost will remain constant.
5. Products have costs and those costs will remain constant.

Assumption 1 begs the obvious question what would be the impact if the five additional setups required by the 50-part lot size from Figure 2.15 were made with excess capacity? If this were the case, there would be no difference in the cost of the setup for each lot size. This an important issue. Additional setup does not necessarily create additional expense. Since the objective of the EOQ formula is sub-optimization between the cost of setup and the cost associated with carrying inventory we need to go no further. The formula is unreliable. It cannot predict the actual impact of various lot sizes from an economic perspective. It does not consider the impact of capacity in the calculation of the lot size or on the profitability of the company.

Assuming that setup costs will remain constant for a particular lot size (assumption 2) ignores the fact that in some cases the additional setups will be made on resources which have excess capacity. Other times the exact same lot size and part will be made on resources which use protective or productive capacity. In the later case, the cost incurred is a result of either an increase in operating expense due to overtime, an increase in inventory due to parts being released earlier or a decrease in the creation of throughput.

Assuming that a specific lot size will remain constant (assumption 3) is also questionable given that any lot may be split multiple times during the manufacturing process. The EOQ formula assumes that the process and transfer batch will always remain the same.

Assuming that carrying cost will remain constant (assumption 4) or that products have cost (assumption 5) presupposes that the cost of a product even exists in order to create the carrying cost figure or that a particular rate of cost can be predicted.

The whole concept that products cost a certain amount stems from the idea that this information can be used to make decisions. If decisions cannot be made based on the cost of a product, then cost as an entity becomes irrelevant. It is merely an illusion. When the amount of money spent to gather cost data or the economic impact of the poor decisions that result from it are considered, it becomes a very expensive illusion to maintain

Cost accounting was created 100 years ago to solve problems in an environment which no longer exists. Nowhere in cost accounting is the concept of capacity discussed, and yet this is the overall governing factor which must guide the decision process. See Chapter 5, "Correcting the Decision Process," of *The Next Phase of Total Quality Management* and also *The Haystack Syndrome* for further background discussion.

Additional Considerations

Other lot sizing techniques not attempting to sub-optimize but which are used in MRP include

- Lot for lot
- Fixed order quantity

While these techniques do not suffer from the illusions of reducing cost through lot sizing, they still represent static data and make the assumption that the process and transfer batches must be the same.

These are issues which are not necessarily caused by the lot sizing algorithm chosen, but rather by the way MRP works. During gross to net requirements generation no attempt is made to determine what lot size will maximize throughput at the constraint, yet this is a very important step within the five-step process.

Conclusion to the Lot Sizing Problem

Since the governing methodology behind the information system is to help in the overall implementation of the five steps of improvement, any discussion of lot sizing must begin there. The key issue must be the impact of a given lot size on the exploitation of the constraint and the ability for the remaining resources to subordinate to the way in which it has been decided to exploit the constraint. It is only in the attempt to actually accomplish this task that the right lot size can be found (see Chapter 6).

Additionally, the true test to determine success or failure of a specific lot sizing strategy will be the impact of the strategy on the three measurements of throughput, inventory and operating expense. Will there be a change to these measurements as a result of a specific lot size? The key questions to ask in order to solve the lot sizing problem are

- Will the particular lot size make inventory go up or down?
- Will there be a need for more or less operating expense?
- Will throughput be enhanced or will it decline?

If an answer cannot be determined for these three questions, then a satisfactory lot size cannot be determined. The question becomes what are the factors in the manufacturing environment which impact a given lot size?

CAPACITY REQUIREMENTS PLANNING

Capacity requirements planning (CRP) takes the output of MRP and, by using the work center and route files, time phases the order in which specific activity is to take place on a given set of resources. The objective is to ensure that adequate capacity is available to meet the detailed schedule of material created by MRP (see Figure 2.16).

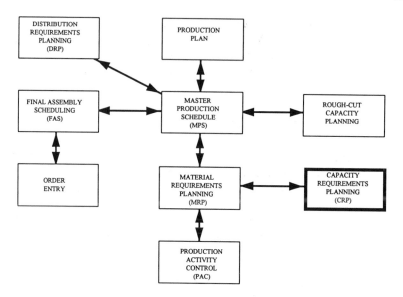

Figure 2.16 The closed loop system—capacity requirements planning.

After obtaining the output of MRP (Figure 2.17), capacity requirements planning reads the route file (Figure 2.18) to obtain the demand requirements for specific parts at their respective operations and work centers. This time is then multiplied by the amount of the order and then placed into time buckets (Figure 2.19).

In Figure 2.17 10 part As are planned for release in periods 2, 3 and 5. According to the routing, each part will consume 1.0 hour of assembly time and

Part: A	1	2	3	4	5	6
Planned Releases	0	10	10	0	10	0
LT = 2 Lot = 10						

Figure 2.17 The output of MRP.

Part No.	Oper. No.	Work Center	S/U Hrs.	Run Hrs.	Move Hrs.	Q/Days.
A	010	Asmb.	1	1.0	0.3	5.0
	020	Test	2	1.0	0.3	2.0
	030	Insp.	1	1.0	0.3	3.0

Figure 2.18 The route file.

each order will have 1.0 hour of setup. With a lead time of two periods, the 11 hours total time for each order is placed in periods 3, 4 and 6.

Setting aside the issue that capacity requirements planning inherits the static time phasing created by material requirements planning, CRP suffers from the same problem as rough-cut capacity planning. Hours are dropped into buckets and aggregated against time that is not available.

Looping Back to the MPS

The idea of looping back to the master schedule and correcting a capacity requirements problem at this point is useless. No real information has been collected to make that decision. However, even when this is attempted and a new master schedule is set the impact is very unpredictable. Since each operation in the routing is permanently connected by individual start and stop times, whenever a change is made to alter the load on one resource the change is also made on other resources. Unloading a resource which is loaded to greater than 100% may create problems on other resources (see Figure 2.20).

Work Center	1	2	3	4	5	6
Assembly			11	11		11

Figure 2.19 Computing the load.

	R-1	R-2	R-3	R-4
Order A	10	20	10	10
Order B	10	20	10	10
Order C				
Total Hours	20	40	20	20
Load	80%	120%	85%	70%
Period 9				

Figure 2.20   Unloading the MPS.

Orders **A** and **B** create a load on resources R-1 through R-4 in period 9. Since resource R-2 appears to be loaded to 120% the master schedule must be leveled so that R-2's time is reduced to at least 100%. To accomplish this task order **B** is shifted in time so that it starts in period 10 instead of 9. Originally, the orders in period 10 did not create an overload problem. After the shift a problem was created when **B**'s labor requirements were added to **C** (see Figure 2.21).

Resource R-1 is now loaded to 120% and resource R-3 is now loaded to 167% in period 10. The problem is discovered only after running MPS, MRP and CRP programs. So another iteration must be tried. The master schedule is adjusted and then the MPS, MRP and CRP programs are run again.

The really interesting part about this process is that even if a master schedule is eventually set to a level load, the load indications are still bogus because of the problems already discussed. To this point the entire procedure has been an exercise in futility

PRODUCTION ACTIVITY CONTROL

Shop Floor Control

The "objective of the shop floor control system (SFC) is to execute the material plan" (*Manufacturing Planning and Control Systems,* 1988). It takes the output

	R-1	R-2	R-3	R-4
Order A				
Order B	10	20	10	10
Order C	20	10	30	10
Total Hours	30	30	40	20
Load	120%	90%	167%	70%
Period 10				

Figure 2.21 Unloading the MPS.

of material requirements planning and actually schedules the factory by setting the priority for orders in each work center. SFC, also called production activity control (PAC), represents the connection between the individual work centers on the shop floor and all that has occurred so far within the planning process (see Figure 2.22).

Dispatching

Scheduling priority instructions are passed to individual workers or groups of workers via the dispatch report (see Figure 2.23). Notice that work center R-1 has 4 work orders to be processed for week 24. Notice also that the total load is currently 77.50 hours and that the priority ratings are from .75 to 1.50.

Though the dispatch report shown uses critical ratio to determine the priority of work, dispatch lists can use a number of different methodologies to create the priority arrangement of orders, including

- Slack time
- Slack time per operation
- Critical ratio
- Shortest operation next
- First come, first serve
- Operation start time
- Due date

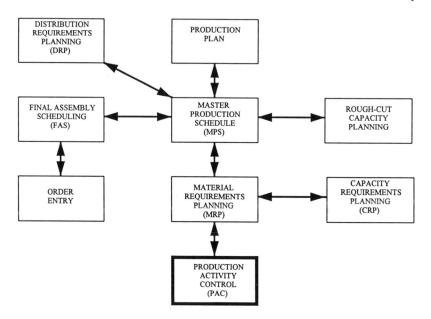

Figure 2.22   The closed loop system—production activity control.

Dispatch Report

Work Center: R-1   Desc. Mill   Week 24

Work Order	Part No.	Oper.	Description	Qty	Hours	Priority
W/O1234	PN456A	10	Mill	50	25.00	.75
W/O1235	PN456B	10	Mill	30	15.00	.98
W/O1236	PN456C	10	Mill	25	12.50	1.03
W/O1237	PN456D	10	Mill	50	25.00	1.50

Total Load   77.50

Figure 2.23   The dispatch report.

- Next queue
- Least setup

Each one of these methods has different focusing mechanisms and will create a specific outcome different than the next, such as reducing the number of jobs in queue or insuring that the next queue is full. However, the objective of shop floor control must be to "exploit the constraint and to subordinate the remaining resources to the way in which it has been decided to exploit the constraint." This is not what is intended by these methods, which thus serve to undermine the planning process.

Slack time subtracts the sum of the remaining processing time from the time remaining. Time remaining is determined by subtracting the current date and time from the due date and time. Those orders which have the least slack are given the highest priority.

The *critical ratio* method creates a ratio by determining the time remaining between the current date and the due date, then dividing this number by the lead time remaining. Obviously, the lower the number the higher the priority.

Shortest operation next concentrates on reducing the number of orders in the queue by taking those orders that can be finished the quickest.

First come, first serve takes orders as they arrive and processes them regardless of need.

The *operation start time* and *due date* scheduling methods attempt to minimize lateness by concentrating on the time orders are to be shipped to the customer.

Next queue looks for the shortest queue in the process after the current operation and feeds material to it so that downstream resources never run out of orders to process.

Least setup looks at those orders with the least amount of time required to perform a setup operation. Similar in objective to the shortest operation next technique, least setup attempts to lower the overall number of orders in the queue by choosing those orders which have the lowest setup or where setup can be saved by processing two orders together with only one setup. The thought process is that the less time spent on setup and the more that is spent on production, the better the company will be financially. In addition, the assumption is made that reducing the number of orders at each work center will cause profits to increase.

These techniques can be categorized in two ways:

- Those which use local measurements to guide the decision of what orders to process next, such as shortest operation next, least setup and next queue
- Those which are based on due date criteria, such as critical ratio, operation start and due date and slack time.

In maximizing local measurements it is hoped to maximize the global measurement of return on investment by reducing cost or minimizing queue time. Those sequencing techniques which use local measurements to guide the decision on what orders to process next have no basis on reality and from a global perspective can do more harm than good. They do not recognize that both parts and resources must be synchronized to maximize the generation of throughput.

As an example, next queue ignores the fact that the operation with the greatest queue may be the constraint and that the operation with the lowest queue may be a non-constraint. Since the main issue of this technique is not to synchronize and protect those orders which will generate throughput, mismatched parts that must be assembled with those coming from the constraint will cause throughput to drop immediately.

Least setup suffers from the same problem as next queue and is a myopic way of looking at scheduling. If every work center used this kind of scheduling without interference in the way of expediting orders, the company would soon have no choice but to close its doors and declare itself insolvent. Reducing the total amount of orders at a work center rather than concentrating on exploitation or subordination means an overabundance of mismatched parts.

Those techniques which are based on a due date performance issue will probably be more effective in meeting the objective of satisfying the customer, but are not constructed from a complete understanding of how resources impact each other (*relationships between resources*) or what actions are necessary to accomplish the activities of exploitation or subordination. And yet, this is what must be done.

For those techniques which use due date performance the question must be asked: to what date is the order to perform? There are a number of issues:

- In order to protect the schedule on the constraint the processing start and stop time of an order which is prior to arriving at the constraint must be to the constraint's schedule.
- In order to arrive at a proper start time for any operation there must be an aggregation of those things which can go wrong.
- In order to arrive at a proper start time there must be an understanding of what the current load is on the resource in question and whether or not it threatens the constraint's ability to generate throughput.
- If the schedule for the order is at the constraint, then the sequencing of orders must be based on the concept of maximizing throughput at the constraint.

In any discussion of the sequencing techniques mentioned, no discussion of how resources interface and the resulting impact on the schedule are ever given. In addition, there is an overwhelming assumption that no constraint exists or, that if it does, there will be no impact on how sequencing is to take place.

The objective of any scheduling policy must be to maximize the throughput generated by the constraint and to protect it. From a global perspective the techniques mentioned do not accomplish or help to accomplish this task.

Statistical Fluctuation in Shop Floor Control

If each order within the schedule occupies a specific place in time and at the same time each resource fluctuates in its ability to deliver, the result is a situation where sometimes orders are delivered early and sometimes orders are delivered late. This is a naturally occurring phenomenon any time there is a schedule. Notice that in Figure 2.24 the opportunity to be early is just as great as the opportunity to be late.

There is a naturally occurring bell shaped curve. However, sometimes this curve moves to the right because of the impact other resources have when not delivered to this resource on time. Sometimes, even though the resource received its order early, it is not able to deliver on time due to something which occurred at this resource or because of its current load or both. These are naturally occurring statistical fluctuations and can be predicted as well as planned

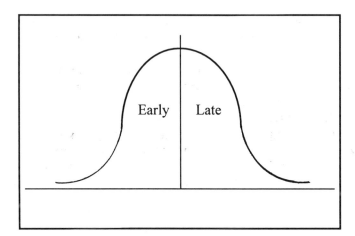

Figure 2.24   Statistical fluctuation in shop floor control.

for. What cannot be planned for is human interdiction which prevents these events from occurring.

By distributing a dispatch report, this naturally occurring phenomenon can be circumvented rather than simply planned for. Unfortunately, it is human nature which consistently prevents orders from being early. By providing a start or due date, operators are not only being told when something is on time or late, but they are also told when something should not be started early. The problem here is that the impact of not starting a job early can only be detected in aggregate. In other words, unless it is known what the cumulative impact is across all resources, a decision cannot be made. In absence of this information it is better to be early whenever possible so that those resources which cannot perform, for whatever reason, are protected.

The issue is not that people will tend to slow down if they are early, although sometimes this is the case, but that nature abhors a vacuum and in the absence of sufficient motivation they will find what to them or their boss will be a higher priority. What is not realized is that being early from a global perspective can be very important. What is also not realized is that the current method of dispatching can be very detrimental (see Figure 2.25).

Since each operation will fluctuate in delivery and the only side of the fluctuation that is allowed to occur is the late, the cumulative effect of not allowing resources to be early is that orders will be chronically late.

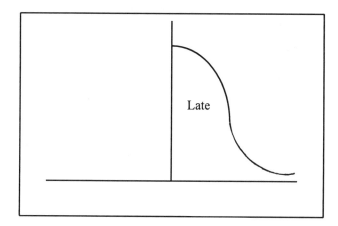

Late

Figure 2.25 Statistical fluctuation in shop floor control.

The real challenge is in finding out which resources need priority instructions and which do not. Certainly for those resources which have excess capacity, the dispatch list is detrimental to the goal of the company. For those which are loaded to 90% or better, it is probably mandatory.

Dynamic Versus Static Data in Shop Floor Control

Lead time typically includes:

- Setup time—the time required to prepare a resource for work
- Run time—the time required to produce a particular part
- Move time—the time spent after an operation moving the part to the next operation in the routing
- Queue time—the time spent waiting at a work center before that work is performed

Figure 2.26 represents a typical routing used in computing the lead time for a particular order. An order of 10 part As at operation 10 will need 1 hour for setup, 10 hours for run time, 0.3 hours for move and 5 days queue time for a total lead time of 6 days plus 3.3 hours, or approximately 6.5 days. Operation 20 will take 2 hours setup, 10 hours run, 0.3 hours move and 2 days queue time for a total lead time of approximately 3.5 days. Operation 30 will need 1 hour for setup, 10 hours for run time, 0.3 hours move and 3 days queue time for a total of approximately 4.5 days. The total lead time for part A is 14.5 days with queue time being almost 70% of the total lead time.

Part No.	Oper. No.	Work Center	S/U Hrs.	Run Hrs.	Move Hrs.	Q/Days
A	010	Asmb.	1	1.0	0.3	5.0
	020	Test	2	1.0	0.3	2.0
	030	Insp.	1	1.0	0.3	3.0
B	010	Asmb.	1	1.0	0.3	5.0
	020	Test	2	1.0	0.3	2.0
	030	Insp.	1	0.50	0.3	3.0

Figure 2.26   Routing.

As seen, queue time is a very critical element in shop floor control. In most companies queue time makes up an average 80% of all lead time within the factory. Eliminated, it would mean that lead times in the factory would be 20% of the current figure. A lead time of one month is now less than a week, but how often is this number actually reviewed? Typically, queue time is maintained in the route file for each step in the operation. The question is how often are these data maintained. It is a full 80% of all lead time and is mostly ignored . . . and for good reason. If a company has 4000 manufactured items with an average of five steps per routing, that's 20,000 individual record locations to manage so that 80% of your lead times are correct. This raises some key questions:

- How often is it monitored?
- If it is input for each part at each operation, how effectively can it be monitored?
- How often does it really change?
- Is there a better way?

The chances of these data being monitored effectively fall into two categories: slim and none. However, there are even greater problems. Since the true objective is to go from the gating operation to the creation of throughput the real issue is not the impact of those things which can go wrong "Murphy" (see *The Haystack Syndrome*) on an individual operational basis, but the aggregate impact of Murphy across all operations. If queue time is placed between resources on an individual basis and then never allowed to change as the dynamics of the situation dictate, then it is at best a waste of time.

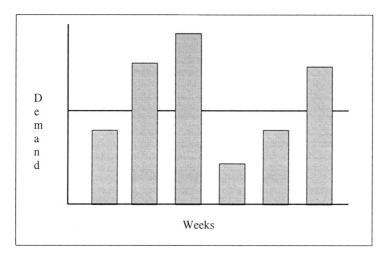

Figure 2.27 Infinite loading.

Finite Loading

Finite loading creates a detailed schedule of all orders and all work centers with stop and start dates assigned for each operation. The start and stop dates are computed using of the output from MRP combined with lead times generated for each open or planned order. In addition, as the sequencing for each operation is generated, the amount of load on each resource is also determined. With infinite loading the placement of the load is unlimited by the amount of capacity available (see Figure 2.27). With finite loading the placement of the load is limited by the amount of capacity available (see Figure 2.28).

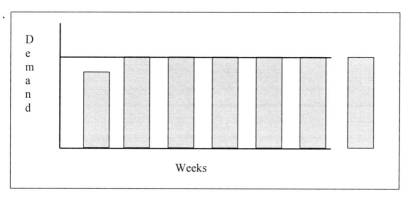

Figure 2.28 Finite loading.

Notice that in the first period, finite loading did not fill all the available capacity. However, beginning in the second period demand is pushed into succeeding periods (the future) so that it does not exceed capacity. Notice also that an additional period is used to absorb the demand as it is pushed out of period 6 into period 7. This method is known as finite set forward.

The Failure of Finite Loading

Finite loading presents some interesting problems. While it attempts to act in a rational manner by assuming that resources should not be loaded past their ability to produce, it fails in the attempt to solve the scheduling problem. The assumptions upon which finite loading was originally created were to use the output of MRP to generate a basic schedule and then augment by not allowing resources to be overloaded. At the same time it was to maximize resource utilization. This is fundamentally unsound for any number of reasons.

- By pushing the load into later periods, it fails to protect the constraint in period 1.
- It is a victim of the static data used to generate the output of MRP.
- It also uses static data, including queue time between resources, from the route file during the scheduling process.
- It attempts to schedule all resources simultaneously.

If the creators of the finite loading process understood the impact of those laws which govern the way resources interface, they would have used as a prerequisite the first three steps of the five-step process of improvement. This is the model from which all systems must begin their development. Any system which does not use this process cannot successfully schedule the factory.

For a scheduling system to be effective it must be capable of

- Identifying the constraint
- Aiding in its exploitation
- Subordinating the remaining resources to the way in which it has been decided to exploit the constraint

This is fundamental and absolute. If a system is incapable of these three steps, it is incapable of successfully scheduling the factory. As seen in Chapter 3, if a system cannot produce a valid schedule, it cannot be used to make decisions.

In the discussion thus far, no portion of the system has been able to identify the constraint. Finite loading has not changed this issue. That is not its objective.

Obviously, if the constraint has not been found, it cannot be exploited. But for discussion purposes suppose that the constraint has been identified. What is it about finite loading which aides in the exploitation process? It creates a schedule. However to exploit means to squeeze the maximum out of the constraint. There is no evidence that finite loading uses any methodology to accomplish this task. If so, in any discussion of finite loading there would also be discussions of issues such as setup savings at the constraint.

Additionally, since finite loading schedules all resources simultaneously, it seems highly unlikely that a decision process needed to accomplish the exploitation and subordination phases could be done effectively. It is only after the exploitation phase is complete that any schedule can be created for the remaining resources. This means that a complete schedule is created by an iterative process. First the constraint is identified and exploited, then the remaining resources are subordinated. During the subordination process other resources may be found with a high probability of being chronically late in supplying the constraint. This is only possible after finding out what the constraint needs.

CONCLUSION

It is obvious at this point that the original assumptions upon which the traditional MRP II system was built were, are and will continue to be erroneous. For the traditional system to fulfill its mission it must change. It must begin the migration process from data system to information system. However, apart from pointing toward some very basic issues such as the measurement system and the five steps of improvement, little has been accomplished so far other than to discredit some portions of MRP II. Building an information system based on reality is something else. How should it function? Upon what basis should it be built? At this point it is important to establish some basics that can be used to logically deduce what an information system for the manufacturing environment should do and how it should function.

STUDY QUESTIONS

1. Define the content and the objective of the master production schedule.

2. Describe rough-cut capacity planning and explain why it fails in attaining it's objective.

3. Explain the input and output of the traditional MRP system.

4. Configure a gross to net requirements generation matrix. Explain how it works and why it fails to attain its objective.

5. Define three types of capacity that will have a major impact on how a factory should be scheduled.

6. What is the cascading effect and what is its impact on MRP?

7. What is the difference between a process and a transfer batch and what determines the optimal size for each?

8. Describe the premise behind the economic order quantity (EOQ) formula and list four assumptions which will invalidate it as a lot sizing alternative.

9. Define capacity requirements planning and explain how it works.

10. Give a brief explanation of the aggregation of demand and describe its impact on the CRP process.

11. What is meant by "looping back to the MPS" and what major flaw(s) is at work during the process?

12. Define shop floor control and the role of the dispatch report.

13. Name four priority methods commonly used in the traditional dispatching system, their objectives, and why they fail in meeting those objectives.

14. Describe the impact of statistical fluctuations on shop floor control and why dispatch lists can sometimes do more harm than good.

15. Describe the impact of static data on lead time in shop floor control.

16. What is finite loading and why does it fail to create an adequate schedule?

3

Establishing the Characteristics of an Information System

What should a manufacturing information system do? This is not a trivial question. Stating that it should schedule the factory, compute material requirements or create a master schedule is not enough to answer the question. The system may need to accomplish these tasks, but if these are the criteria by which the system is designed, it will probably be subject to major flaws. To really understand what an information system should do requires careful consideration.

CHAPTER OBJECTIVES

- To create an understanding of the characteristics of an information system
- To create a relationship between the information system and the decision process
- To understand the organization of the system

DISTINGUISHING BETWEEN DATA AND INFORMATION

In order to build an information system there must be a distinction between what is called *data* and what is called *information*. As mentioned in Chapter 1, information is the answer to a specific question asked, while data are everything else in the system. This is a very important clue. It means that in order to create an information system there must be an understanding of the decision process to be used. This can serve to be a major stumbling block for most developers. The decision process has proven to be very much different than what has been taught for the last 50 to 100 years. However, in building an information system the developer must be able to make this distinction. There must be knowledge of what questions to ask and how decisions are made. The first step in understanding how decisions should be made is to determine the goal of the system.

DEFINING THE GOAL

To be effective, an information system must help a company attain its goal. Obviously, it is important to have a definition of what the company goal should be. For the purposes of this book an assumption will be made that the goal of the company will be to "make more money now as well as in the future" (*The Haystack Syndrome*, 1990).

Since this statement has had major impact on what an information system should do and is actually the basis for the system's creation, it's very important to understand what it really means. If the objective of the company is to make money and a system is needed to help in the process, the definition of the system would be much different than a system designed to help a company make more money now as well as in the future. The key words being *more* and *in the future*. For a company to *make money now* might mean that a system would be needed to help sell all the assets of the company. Once accomplished, the company would not be capable of creating additional money in the future. Making *more money* means that the company wishes to make more money than it is currently capable of making. A system to accomplish this task will be different than that required to maintain the current flow.

ESTABLISHING THE APPROACH

The question which must be asked at this point is what must a company do to accomplish its goal? Answering this question will help considerably to further define the characteristics of the system. The physical laws of the company involve what is called the *dependent variable environment*. The dependent variable environment refers to the environment which has multiple resources depending on each other, and each resource fluctuates in its ability to perform. Since each company is made of chains of events that occur as a result of the interaction of multiple resources, the laws involving dependency and statistical fluctuation dictate how they will interact.

The only valid method of improvement for this environment is the five-step process of improvement defined in *The Haystack Syndrome.* If this is the method by which a company intends to improve and an information system is desired to help in this effort, then it stands to reason that an information system designed to help the company attain its goal should be based on the five step process:

1. Identifying the constraint
2. Exploiting the constraint
3. Subordinating the remaining resources
4. Elevating the constraint
5. Repeating the process

From a design perspective this is actually very good news. This means that the creation of the information system can be accomplished iteratively. The first step is creating the ability to identify the constraint. The second step is to exploit it. And so on. If each step can be accomplished successfully without creating new logistical or policy constraints, then the development of the information system will be successful.

EXPANDING THE DEFINITION

Because the information system must deal with the physical attributes of the environment in which it must work, the previous goal requires expanding. To be effective the system must help the company "make more money now as well as in the future," *given the current situation.*

This addition to the statement adds another dimension. If a system is to be based on the current situation, it stands to reason that the current situation be known. This is a major clue to another of the characteristics of the system. *It should resemble the environment in which it must perform.* To do this it should be capable of re-creating the physical laws which govern the environment in question. To ensure that the system can perform its function means that it should *not* contain within its design any logistical or policy constraints. This is why it is so important to eliminate those characteristics in the traditional MRPII system.

Note: companies that operate on a different principle such as a not-for-profit basis may have a different goal and therefore may have a different definition of what an information system should be.

THE INFORMATION SYSTEM AND
THE DECISION PROCESS

Much of a company's problems (90–99%) in attempting to implement the five steps will surface in the form of policy constraints. In other words, for whatever reason and no matter what level of the company, a decision will be made not to make more money. This sounds rather amazing until it is considered that most people are still working with the inertia created by cost accounting and are usually unaware that they have made a decision or taken a specific action that will hurt their company. In fact, even when presented with clear-cut evidence to the contrary, people will insist that they were correct. This is one of the main reasons why changing a company can be so difficult. However, if information is the answer to a specific question, then it is not until after a close examination of the decision process is made that an information system can be built. The following examples demonstrate some of the issues.

Making a Sales Decision—Accepting an Order

The traditional decision process uses the difference between standard cost and the sales price (see Figure 3.1). If the sales price does not exceed standard cost by a given percentage, the salesman turns down the offer. However, as seen in Chapter 5 of *The Next Phase of Total Quality Management* (1994), what the salesman really needs to know to make the decision is much different. It includes:

				Standard		
Material		Labor	Overhead	Cost		
100	+	50	+	100	=	250

		Standard		
Sales		Standard		
Price		Cost	Margin	
350	–	250	=	100

Figure 3.1 Making a sales decision.

- The lowest throughput per unit of the constraint that is currently being produced
- How much throughput per unit of the constraint will be generated by the new order
- Whether the new order will use excess or protective capacity by producing the product internally
- Whether accepting the new order will create a new constraint

Note: throughput per unit of the constraint is computed as the sales price minus raw material divided by the total constraint time for the product.

In order to help the salesman make a decision the system must determine:

- The constraint
- The amount of time each product spends on the constraint
- The cost of raw material for the product being produced
- The impact of using excess capacity
- The impact of using protective capacity

Since a key ingredient in solving the decision process has been in understanding the impact of the constraints of the system and the impact of protective or excess capacity, to fulfill these requirements demands that a valid schedule be produced which will be capable of determining, for instance, where the constraint is.

Making a Quality Decision—Scrap Versus Rework

Another type of decision needing an answer is scrap versus rework. Would it be better from a global perspective to scrap a particular product or rework it (see Figure 3.2).

A sales order for 100 product As each sold for $100, has a raw material content of $25 and is processed on the constraint. After processing 50% of the parts, 10 are found to be defective. Reworking the parts will use an additional 10 minutes of constraint time and $5 worth of raw material. The question is, should these parts be scrapped or reworked and what information is needed to make the decision.

If the parts are scrapped, then of course they must be replaced. The original parts plus the remaining 50 must be produced creating $4,500 worth of throughput and using 900 minutes of constraint time. The scrapped parts will

PRODUCT	CCR TIME/UNIT	CCR TIME AVAIL
A	15	1500 MIN
ORDER = 100	SP = $100	RM = $25
DEFECTIVE PARTS	TIME/UNIT	MATERIAL
10	10	$5

Figure 3.2 The quality decision—data.

require additional raw material totaling $250 that must be subtracted from the total throughput generated. Throughput per unit of the constraint is therefore $4,250 divided by 900 minutes, or $4.72 per minute earned from the constraint (see Figure 3.3).

				(T)	CCR TIME
THROUGHPUT	=	$60(100-25)$	=	$4,500	900
MATERIAL	=	10×25	=	$ 250	
				$4,250	900

$$T/uc = \frac{\$4,250}{900} = \$4.72$$

Figure 3.3 The quality decision—throughput per unit of constraint if parts are scrapped.

				(T)	CCR TIME
THROUGHPUT	=	10 (100 - 30)	=	$700	100
THROUGHPUT	=	50 (100 - 25)	=	$3,750	750
				$4,450	850

$$T/uc \ = \ \frac{\$4,450}{850} \ = \ \$5.23$$

Figure 3.4   The quality decision—throughput per unit of constraint if re-worked.

Figure 3.4 shows the result if the ten product As are reworked. Ten As are processed on the constraint for 10 minutes using 100 minutes of constraint time and $5 additional raw material. Throughput generated is $700. The remaining 50 pieces are processed using 750 minutes and creating $3,750 in throughput. Total throughput generated is $4,450 and the total time used on the constraint is 850 minutes. Throughput per unit of the constraint is $5.23.

Since the throughput per unit of the constraint is higher for rework, the parts should be reworked.

What was needed to make this decision?

- The total amount of throughput that was to be generated by either scrap or rework (throughput = sales price – raw material)
- The amount of time to be used on the constraint for either scrap or rework

To help the foreman the system must be able to determine

- The constraint
- The amount of time each product spends on the constraint
- The cost of raw material for the product being produced
- The impact of using excess capacity
- The impact of using protective capacity

ESTABLISHING THE MEASUREMENTS

The effectiveness of any information system must be judged in the context of how well the system is able to aid the company in performing relative to its goal. The global measurement of return on investment provides adequate proof that the system is accomplishing its primary function. However, it does not provide a method of focusing improvements so that the company understands what is required to reach its goal. In other words, if a decision is to be made at a local level to improve the performance of the company, return on investment will help to determine the impact of the decision, but it will not help determine what to improve. To do this will require that local measurements be established. This was the original objective of cost accounting, but those systems which have relied on cost accounting to make decisions have been greatly disparaged . . . and for good reason.

Not only has the effectiveness of cost accounting and activity based accounting been disproved, but the procedures have been determined to be the root cause of major problems leading to poor corporate performance.

The traditional measurements of effectiveness used at the local level can actually prevent the generation of valid decisions.

In order to understand what will be necessary to improve the company relative to its goal, local measurements must be employed which can be readily predictable from a global perspective. The measurements of choice are:

- Throughput—the rate the system generates money through sales
- Inventory—all the money invested in purchasing the things the system intends to sell
- Operating expense—all the money the system spends in turning *inventory* into *throughput*

These measurements were presented by Dr. Eli Goldratt in his book *The Race* (1986) and, as seen in *The Haystack Syndrome*, are an important ingredient in defining how an information system should work. The key issue when answering a question for a company whose goal is to "make more money now as well as in the future" is what will be the impact on throughput, inventory, and operating expense given a specific action? To create an information system these questions must be answered. In addition, the system must be capable of focusing efforts in proper order. Since "inventory and operating expense exist to produce and protect the throughput figure, understanding more about what is to be done to improve throughput is a prerequisite to dealing with the other two measurements" (*The Next Phase of Total Quality Management*)

THE ORGANIZATION OF THE SYSTEM

It should be clear by now that in order to simulate the decision process, or to answer the "what if" questions, there must be a *valid schedule*. However, it is not enough just to create a schedule. The schedule must be protected from those things which can go wrong. This protection must take into consideration where the protection is needed and be dynamic in nature so that it can change as the situation dictates. It must be capable of *controlling* the activity of the non-constraints so that they are subordinated to the constraint. So the organization of the system should be as follows:

- Schedule—identifies the system's constraints, exploits them and subordinates the activity of the non-constraints
- Control—compensates for those things which will go wrong
- What if—replaces cost accounting in answering questions

SUMMARY

Since the goal of the company plays a major roll in what an information system should do, the real issue becomes what the goal of the company is and what the physical laws dictate must be done in order to improve.

An effective information system designed for this environment should

- Aid in the implementation of the five steps of improvement
- Resemble the environment by re-creating the physical laws which govern it
- Use a measurement system which is based on reality
- Be void of any policy constraints

STUDY QUESTIONS

1. Define the goal of an information system.

2. Describe the connection between the goal of the information system and its basic structure.

3. What is the distinction between what is called data and what is called information?

4. What is the connection between the information system and the decision process?

5. What is the formula for computing throughput per unit of the constraint and why is it important?

6. What must a salesman know to make a determination of whether to accept an order and how does this differ from the traditional view?

7. List and explain the three absolute measurements defined by the theory of constraints.

8. Explain why these three measurements are important.

9. What is the dependent variable environment and what is its impact on the information system?

4

Defining the Structure

This chapter presents the structure of the system from the global perspective and defines the individual relationships of each segment, including input and output requirements.

CHAPTER OBJECTIVES

- To provide a global picture of how the system is to be structured
- To define the input and output relationships

THE THEORY OF CONSTRAINTS BASED SYSTEM

Figure 4.1 is a diagram of the theory of constraints (TOC) based system designed to implement the five steps of improvement. Notice that the master schedule still drives the input to the system. It is a logical place from which to combine forecast and sales order data, show available to promise (ATP) for future sales requirements, and relate the status of orders.

However, unlike MRP II, rather than serving as the input to material requirements planning, the output of the MPS will be the input to the process designed to identify the primary constraint. To properly schedule the factory the new system must be capacity sensitive, and since a valid schedule must be generated based on the system's constraints, the first step is to identify the

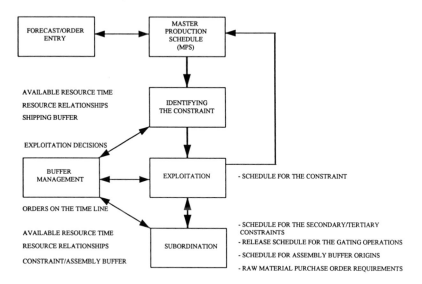

Figure 4.1   The TOC based system.

primary constraint. It is during this process that material is allocated so that requirements will not be generated for material already in the system. The demand for additional raw material and its timing can only be determined after all the constraints have been identified and a schedule created for each. It is only after the needs of the constraints are known that a release schedule can be produced from which to glean the amount of raw material required.

The next step is to use the output of the identification phase to direct exploitation. It is during this phase that the schedule is created for the primary constraint and decisions are made for how the maximum amount of throughput is to be generated. Notice that from the exploitation phase there is a feedback mechanism to update the master schedule. After a firm schedule for the primary constraint has been set, if their are any changes that will require modification of the master schedule, then the new dates can be passed.

Once the schedule has been set, it is important to ensure that not only the remaining resources deliver to the constraint what it needs, but also that the remaining resources do not interfere with the constraint's ability to deliver on time. The subordination phase takes the output of exploitation and subordinates the activities of the remaining resources to the schedule created for the primary constraint. During this process the system attempts to eliminate any conflicts between the constraint and all other resources (see Chapter 7). If the conflicts cannot be eliminated automatically, then the user is given the opportunity to intercede manually. When this fails, conflicting orders on the primary constraint are pushed into the future along with the respective due date.

Buffer management is a methodology for monitoring and controlling the impact of those things which can go wrong (see Chapter 8). As changes occur in the system's ability to respond effectively, the buffer size used as input to identification, exploitation and subordination phases can be increased or decreased to gain or lose protection.

DEFINING THE INPUT TO THE SYSTEM

Identification

The input to the identification phase consists of

- The master production schedule
- Resource relationships
- Available resource capacity
- The shipping buffer

The initial input of the master production schedule is not representative of the traditional MPS. While it consists of a list of end items with relative quantities and due dates, no netting or consolidation of MPS demand into time buckets occurs at this time (see Chapter 11). It usually does *not* represent "what can and will be produced." To this point, no attempt is made to determine any capacity requirements. The MPS is simply a wish list until direct feedback has been received from the final version of the schedule for the primary constraint.

Resource relationships are defined in what is termed *the net*. The net, a creation of the Goldratt Institute, includes the product flow diagrams for all products in the master schedule and is used for computing material requirements, determining which resources are to produce what products, and understanding how resources interface.

Obviously, if a resource limitation is to be identified, the resource availability in time increments must be involved.

Exploitation

The input to the exploitation phase includes

- The sequencing of orders on the time line
- Decisions of how to exploit the constraint
- Setup and run times for each operation
- Available resource capacity

During the identification process, orders are placed on a time line that runs from time zero, or today, to the end of the schedule horizon. After initial placement, the orders are leveled by pushing the demand toward time zero (see Chapter 5). It is the output of this process which is the input to exploitation.

During the exploitation phase, a schedule is created for the constraint. However, by definition, the constraint is a resource which is limited in capacity. If the constraint is to be exploited, decisions must be made to maximize the amount of throughput that can be generated. It is at this time that the system considers issues such as overtime, setup savings and off-loading to maximize resource availability.

While the system can automatically apply or make recommendations of where overtime should be spent and what orders should be combined to save productive capacity, it is the user who must finally decide.

During the exploitation phase, setup and run times are used to determine start and stop times for each order across the constraint and to aid in simulating the decision process by performing tasks such as setup savings.

As in the identification phase, in order to exploit the constraint the availability of the capacity to be applied to each order should be known.

Subordination

The input to the subordination phase includes

- The schedule of the primary constraint (exploitation)
- The relationships between resources
- Available resource capacity
- Constraint/assembly buffers
- Setup and run times

Like identification and exploitation, the relationships between resources, the available resource time, the setup times and run times for each order must be known. However, since the objective of subordination is to deliver to the constraint what it needs, input to subordination must include the demands of the constraint. This means that for those part/operations processed prior to arriving to the constraint, the schedule created during exploitation must be used as input along with the requirements of the master schedule. In addition, the structure must include a method for protecting the constraint. *Constraint buffers* are used to aggregate the impact of those things which can go wrong on those resources which feed the constraint. *Assembly buffers* aggregate the impact of those things which can go wrong on those legs which are not constrained but must deliver parts to be combined in assembly operations with parts from the constraint.

DEFINING THE OUTPUT OF THE SYSTEM

Identification

The output of the identification phase is very simple. It must feed the exploitation phase with

- The identity of the constraint
- Orders on a time line

Without doubt, before the constraint can be exploited it must be identified. During the identification process, orders are placed on the time line for the constraint.

Note: the time line for the constraint is the scheduling horizon.

Exploitation

As discussed the output of the exploitation phase is a schedule for the primary constraint. The schedule includes start and stop times for every order within the planning horizon.

Subordination

The output of subordination includes

- The schedule of the secondary, tertiary and remaining constraints
- The schedule for assembly buffer origins

- The release schedule for the gating operations
- Raw material purchasing requirements

Once the primary constraint has been identified and scheduled those resources which may be unable to deliver to the constraint what it needs due to a lack of adequate protective capacity must themselves be exploited to ensure their ability to deliver to the constraint. Secondary or even tertiary schedules may be produced to accomplish this task.

Note: a key issue in subordinating one schedule to another is to ensure that there are no conflicts between the two.

It is very important that a schedule be set for assembly operations having one leg coming from the constraint and another coming from a non-constraint. The objective is to prevent the possibility of mismatched parts arriving from non-constraining legs and to ensure that once parts have been created on the constraint that they do not wait for parts coming from the non-constraining leg. To perform this function the assembly schedule is used. The assembly schedule coordinates the activity of the assembly buffer origin and determines the release schedule for raw material at the gating operations.

The release of raw material to the gating operations is planned by the subordination phase to ensure the proper sequencing of orders throughout the plant.

Once the releases of orders to the gating operations have been planned, material purchases can be made. The launching of raw material orders is planned using the lead time data stored in the item master for each raw material part plus the release schedule for the gating operations.

ESTABLISHING THE RELATIONSHIPS BETWEEN RESOURCES

As mentioned earlier relationships between resources for the schedule are established by the creation of what is termed *the net*. The net is a re-creation of the way in which products flow through the factory and includes:

- The combination of all product flow diagrams
- Work in process inventory
- Operational setup and run times for which demand appears in the master schedule

INDENTED BILL OF MATERIAL			ROUTING			
			PART	OP.	S/U	RUN
A		MAKE	A	10	10	15
				20	15	5
	B	MAKE		30	10	10
		C	PURCH.	B	10	10	5
				20	15	10
	D	MAKE		30	10	10
		E	PURCH.	D	10	10	15
				20	15	15
				30	10	10

Figure 4.2 Creating the part/operation.

The product flow diagram is a combination of individual part/operations and resources on which the product is to be processed. The part/operation is the smallest building block within the net and is a combination of the bill of material and route files. In one character string the part/operation can identify what part is to be processed at a specific routing step (see Figure 4.2). From the bill of material and route file shown, a combination of part A with operation 10 would create part/operation A/10.

Part/operations are placed in sequence along with resource information to form the product flow diagram The product flow diagram defines how the completed part is to be produced (see Figure 4.3). Notice that purchased part C feeds part/operation B/10 on resource R-6. B/10 feeds B/20 on resource R-5. This process continues until the final product A is complete at A/30 on resource R-1.

Figure 4.4 represents the net. Notice that the flow of the net is the same as the product flow diagram. Raw material part C is received into resource R-6 to perform part/operation B/10. Resource R-6 then feeds resource R-5 through the connection of B/10 to B/20. Additional data within the net include resource run

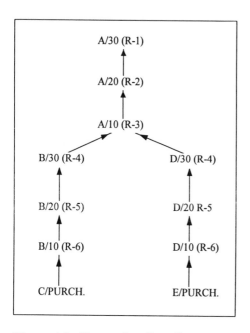

Figure 4.3 The product flow diagram.

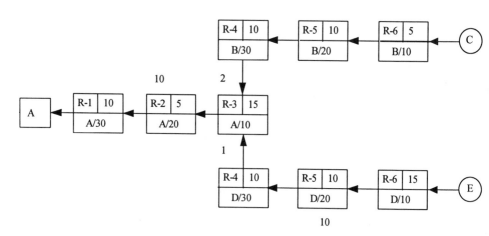

Figure 4.4 The net.

time, bill of material quantity relationships and inventory. Part/operation B/10 is processed on resource R-6 for 5 minutes. There are currently 10 parts which have been completed by D/20 and are ready to be consumed by part/operation D/30. Part/operation A/10 is created by assembling two B/30 parts with 1 D/30 part at resource R-3. (Setup time was not included due to a lack of space.)

As discussed the net is the major source of data used to

- Identify the constraint
- Generate the schedule (exploitation)
- Subordinate the remaining resources

The net provides two major advantages:

- A very large number of data files can be reduced and stored in a very small amount of space within the system.
- The time needed for creating a schedule or determining material requirements can be greatly reduced.

Since the amount of space used is very small in comparison to the vast number of files currently being used, the entire net can be maintained in resident memory. By reducing the amount of I/Os needed for processing, the speed of the system can be greatly enhanced.

SUMMARY

The TOC based information system is very much different from the traditional MRPII system. The basic structure and processes have been greatly modified to include the goal of the corporation as well as the physical laws which govern the manufacturing environment. Additionally, new innovations, like the net, have also been designed to take advantage of new computer technologies and enhance the speed at which information can be obtained.

STUDY QUESTIONS

1. Prepare a schematic of the TOC based system and define the input and output requirements of each segment.

2. Define the term part/operation.

3. Define what is meant by a product flow diagram and explain its primary function.

4. Create a bill of material and routing for one product produced in a typical job shop environment and then prepare a product flow diagram presenting the flow of part/operations involved.

5. What is the net and how is it constructed?

6. What advantage(s) does the net provide in constructing an information system?

7. Define the terms identification, exploitation and subordination in reference to the TOC based manufacturing system and describe their basic functions.

8. Describe the function of buffers, list three different types in relation to the TOC based manufacturing system and define how each are used.

9. What is meant by the term time line?

10. In the TOC based System, how is the master production schedule similar to the way in which it is used in the traditional MRP system?

5

Identifying the Constraint

The primary capacity constrained resource (CCR) is that resource which, more than any other, threatens the creation of throughput. If throughput is to be generated by the delivery of products to shipping then it can be said that the primary CCR is that resource which threatens, more than any other resource, the ability of the system to deliver orders to shipping.

CHAPTER OBJECTIVES

- To present the TOC methodology for identifying the primary capacity constrained resource
- To introduce the role of the shipping buffer
- To create an understanding of the physical phenomena which impact the identification process

IDENTIFYING THE PRIMARY CCR

The Impact of Statistical Fluctuations on the Schedule

All resources are subject to statistical fluctuations in their ability to perform. In other words, sometimes an order will be early and sometimes it will be late. If an order becomes late due to a statistical fluctuation, to correct the problem additional capacity is required to bring the schedule back to its original plan.

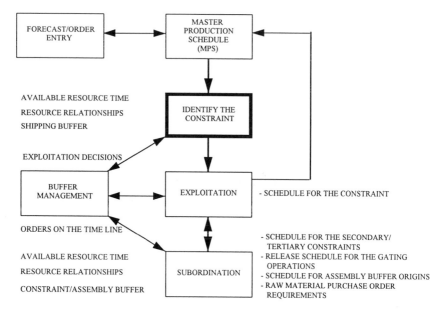

Figure 5.1 The TOC based system—identification.

The capacity required to correct problems in lateness due to normal statistical fluctuation is termed protective capacity. If there is not a sufficient amount of protective capacity to correct for lateness, each time a problem hits orders will become increasingly late. (Figure 5.2).

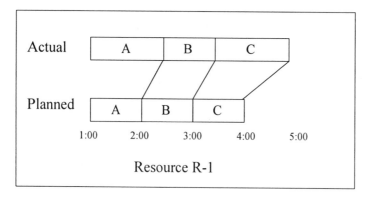

Figure 5.2 The impact of statistical fluctuation on the schedule.

Order A, originally planned for completion at 2:00, did not actually finish until approximately 2:25. A problem occurring on resource R-1 generated a delay of 25 minutes. This means that order B, originally planned to start at 2:00, was not able to start until 2:25. While B is processed in the proper amount of time, the 25 minute delay caused by the original problem has not been corrected. So, order C is also started late. A problem again hits resource R-1 while processing order C. Order C, originally scheduled to be completed at 4:00, is not completed until 4:50 (a delay of 50 minutes).

Notice that there is a cumulative effect. Because Resource R-1 does not have enough protective capacity to apply in correcting this problem each order is finished successively later.

This situation is exacerbated when more than one resource is involved in the process. Not only will orders processed on resource R-1 be chronically late, but this situation will cause orders on succeeding resources to be chronically late (see Figure 5.3).

Resources R-1 through R-4 feed each other from left to right and are each loaded to 90%. In this case, the objective is to process inventory from resource R-1 to resource R-4 on time. But 90% is a relatively high load and the prospect of having a problem result in an order being late on resource R-1 is very high. The demand on resource R-2 is equally as great. Since resource R-1 will be chronically late, it is reasonable to consider that resource R-2 will not always be able to start on time. Since R-2's demand is high and yet it will always start late, the probability that resource R-2's orders will be even later is also high. This process will continue until reaching resource R-4.

The impact to the entire process can be readily visible if the load on each resource were to be converted to an 80% probability. In other words, there is an

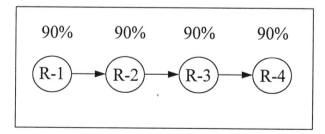

Figure 5.3 The lack of adequate protective capacity.

80% probability of each resource completing its task on time. The combined probability for all resources in Figure 5.3 is .80 to the power of four, or 41%. The string of resources must overcome a 59% probability that the order will be late.

An interesting side note is that the probability of lateness increases in proportion to exactly where in the string processing occurs. At 80%, the probability of lateness is greater for resource R-4 than it is for resource R-2.

It is this phenomenon which helps to identify the primary constraint. That resource which suffers from a lack of protective capacity more than any other has definitely been identified as the prime candidate.

The Role of the Shipping Buffer

As discussed in Chapter 4, a buffer is a time mechanism which acts to aggregate the time required to offset for those things which can go wrong. The shipping buffer offsets for those resources which exist between the primary constraint and shipping. Each order is protected so that no matter what may go wrong most orders will reach shipping on time.

Those resources which, on the whole, suffer from a lack of adequate protective

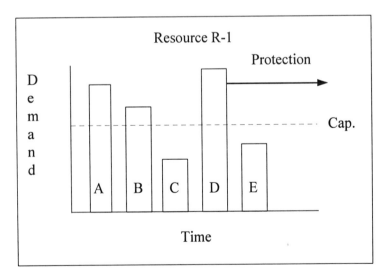

Figure 5.4 Protective capacity.

capacity will tend to have a cumulative effect on the time buffer. So one issue in identifying the constraint is to identify that resource which has the greatest impact on the time buffer in front of shipping (see Figure 5.4).

R-1 has five orders, A through E. Each order has been placed in time so that there is sufficient protection to ensure that they will usually make it to shipping on time. Notice that shipping is to the right. This is also the direction in which the time buffer used to protect shipping has been placed.

Applying Excess Demand

To determine the impact of demand on available protection means applying the time allocated to the orders against the time allocated to protection. However, there is still another issue which plays a part. Simply applying the load by dividing capacity by demand ignores the fact that the time to the right of each order is not available to be applied. To move the excess load to the right would immediately invalidate the delivery to shipping without first looking for more capacity. The only direction in which to apply the excess load is to the left, moving toward time zero (see Figure 5.5).

After the demand has been loaded to a given day on the planning horizon and there is no more capacity available on the resource for that day, the remaining time is applied to the previous day.

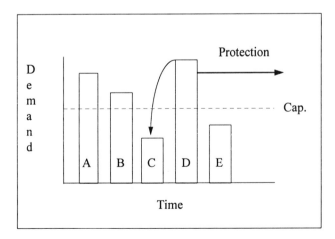

Figure 5.5 Protective capacity—excess load is applied to the left.

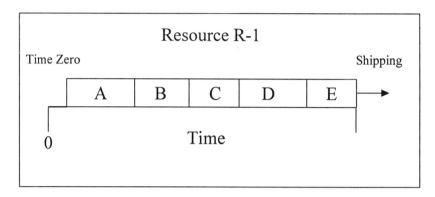

Figure 5.6   Protecting the shipping date.

In Figure 5.6, after applying the excess demand to the left (Figure 5.5) there is still space available before running into time zero (today). Since orders will not need to be displaced and each has its full protection (protection being the length of the shipping buffer), there is more than enough capacity available to reach shipping on time.

Resource R-2 has a similar situation. Notice that R-2's excess demand has been pushed to, but not past, time zero (see Figure 5.7). R-2 will still have all its available protection and will not invalidate any shipping dates. The original protection that was applied to the right still exists.

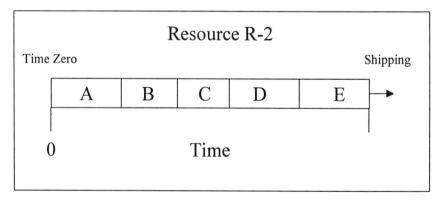

Figure 5.7   Protecting the shipping date—resource R-2.

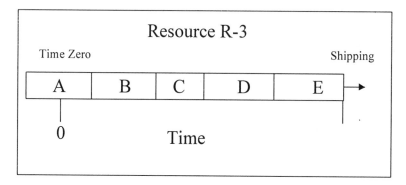

Figure 5.8 Consuming protective capacity.

However, any further increase in the load will begin to impact the amount of protection for those orders which must cross resource R-2.

Consuming Protective Capacity

Notice that R-3's orders have crossed time zero. This means that after applying the required protection to all the orders that must be shipped, there is not enough time available. Since the orders cannot be scheduled past time zero (a physical impossibility), protective time must be consumed to produce R-3's demand (see Figure 5.8).

At this time the primary constraint has yet to be identified. Notice that R-4 has crossed time zero to a greater extent than has R-3 (see Figure 5.9). This means

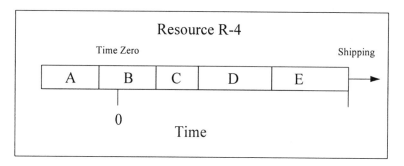

Figure 5.9 Identifying the primary constraint.

that it has even less protective capacity available than R-3. In fact, the demand on R-4 may be large enough that there is not even productive capacity available for some orders.

Among R-1, R-2, R-3 and R-4, the leading candidate to select as the primary constraint is R-4.

Note: this entire concept will be covered in detail later in this chapter.

CREATING THE DATA REQUIREMENTS

The Master Production Schedule

As discussed in Chapter 4, the identification process begins with input from the master production schedule. It is what drives the initial placement of orders on the time line for each resource. Figure 5.10 represents the master production schedule, including demand origination, end item part numbers, quantity and due date. Notice that product A's demand in period 100 originates from sales order S/O111. Notice also that demand for A in period 101 originates from the forecast.

The Shipping Buffer

As discussed earlier, the *shipping buffer* is used during the identification phase to protect the shipping date, plan the initial placement of orders on the time line

DEMAND	PART	QUANTITY	DUE DATE
S/O111	A	20	100
S/O222	F	10	100
S/O333	F	20	101
FORECAST	A	20	101

Figure 5.10   The master production schedule.

```
┌─────────────────────────────────┐
│                                 │
│        BUFFER DATA              │
│                                 │
│     TYPE         LENGTH         │
│    ─────────────────────        │
│                                 │
│    SHIPPING       8 HOURS       │
│                                 │
│    CONSTRAINT    16 HOURS       │
│                                 │
│    ASSEMBLY       8 HOURS       │
│                                 │
└─────────────────────────────────┘
```

Figure 5.11   Buffer data.

during constraint identification, and determine the release time for material which does not go through the constraint. Orders are initially placed using the due date minus the shipping buffer. Figure 5.11 shows the three types of buffers needed to produce the schedule. Notice that the shipping buffer has been set at 8 hours. During the identification phase each order would be offset by 8 hours prior to being placed on the time line. This is done in preparation for the creation of the schedule.

The Net

It is necessary to understand the following:

- Which part/operations will be needed to perform
- In what order the resources are to be used
- Amount of run time needed
- Amount of inventory to apply so that downstream part/operations will not duplicate material that has already been produced.

Figure 5.12 represents the net that is associated with the master schedule presented in Figure 5.10. Since there are two items on the master schedule, the net used earlier has been expanded to include product F.

Note: to save space within the net shown, setup time has been placed with the resource data.

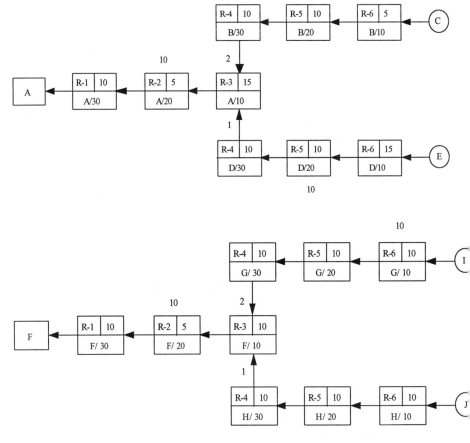

Figure 5.12   The net.

Resource Data

Completing the assemblage of input to the identification phase will require resource capacity data and setup times (see Figure 5.13).

Resource R-1 has 480 minutes per day of productive time and a quantity of one machine. Resource R-4 has 960 minutes per day available with a quantity of two machines.

RESOURCE DATA			
RESOURCE	CAPACITY	S/U	QUANTITY
R-1	480	10	1
R-2	960	15	2
R-3	480	10	1
R-4	960	10	2
R-5	480	15	1
R-6	480	10	1

Figure 5.13 Resource data.

PLACING ORDERS ON THE TIME LINE

Allocating Inventory

Inventory is allocated first come, first serve. Those orders which must be completed first should have priority during processing. Allocating material begins by taking the earliest order in the planning horizon and processing it down the net to determine material requirements.

Processing on the Net

Since processing begins with the earliest order, from the master schedule, 20 product As are due in period 100. According to the net in Figure 5.12, the first Part/operation to be processed is A/30 on resource R-1. Since there is no inventory at A/30 to be used the entire 20 parts must be processed at 10 minutes each. Setup for resource R-1 includes another 10 minutes per order. After offsetting for the shipping buffer by 8 hours, this places a load of 210 minutes on resource R-1 on day 99 (see Figure 5.14).

Part/operation A/20 is next in line to be processed. Notice that there are 10 part/operation A/20s available in inventory to be applied toward the total demand of 20 units created by A/10's requirements. Each of the 10 remaining A/20s to be built requires 5 minutes of run time and 15 minutes of setup for a

Figure 5.14 Processing on the net—resource R-1.

total time of 65 minutes (see Figure 5.15). This time is again placed at the end of the shipping buffer. Notice that in going from A/10 to B/30 within the net there is a bill of material quantity of 2 B/30s needed for every A/10 produced. Bill of material relationships are taken into consideration when processing down the net. B/30's requirements include run time for a quantity of 10 times the bill of material quantity of 2. 20 pieces are processed at 10 minutes each plus a setup of 10 minutes for a total of 210 minutes (see Figure 5.16).

Figure 5.15 Processing on the net—resource R-2.

Figure 5.16 Processing on the net—resource R-4.

Notice that the time frame for each part/operation remains the same for each load placed on each resource. At face value this does not seem logical. How can the load for successive operations appear in the exact same place in time. Remember that *the object of this exercise is not to schedule the factory but to determine which resource is the biggest threat to the creation of throughput.* Remember also that the optimum transfer batch size is quantity one. Since the processing of one part in comparison to the total protective time used in the factory is so small, the difference between where a part would fit on the time line by including the actual processing time or sequencing is minuscule.

Each part/operation within the net is processed similarly for all orders on the MPS. It stops when reaching the last part/operation. While the purchased part quantity requirements are computed during this time, no raw material order timing will be generated until the subordination phase.

Computing Start and Stop Times

Figure 5.17 is a compilation of the data used in computing start and stop times for the initial placement of all orders on the time line for resource R-4. Notice that sales order S/O222 for a quantity of 10 product Fs generated zero time. This is due to the inventory available at part/operation F/20.

The initial placement of B/30 for sales order S/O111 is at the end of day 100 minus the shipping buffer or hour 8:00 on day 99. The start time is set at 4:30 on

Sales Order/Qty	Order Due	Part/ Oper.	Proc. Qty	Setup Time	Run Time	Total Time	Start Time	End Time
S/O111/20	100	B/30	20	10	10	210	99/4:30	99/8:00
		D/30	10	10	10	110	99/6:10	99/8:00
S/O222/10	100	G/30		10	10	0		
		H/30		10	10	0		
S/O333/20	101	G/30	40	10	10	410	100/1:10	100/8:00
		H/30	20	10	10	210	100/4:30	100/8:00
Forecast/20	101	B/30	40	10	10	410	100/1:10	100/8:00
		D/30	20	10	10	210	100/4:30	100/8:00

Figure 5.17   Computing start and stop times.

day 99, a total of 210 minutes earlier than the stop time. The 210 minutes is computed by multiplying the quantity of 20 part requirements by the run time of 10 minutes and adding the 10 minute setup. Once the stop time of the order has been computed, to find the start time simply subtract the total processing time from the stop time.

Accumulating the Demand

As the process continues down the net for each successive order on the master schedule, demand is accumulated for each resource (see Figure 5.18). Order S/O111 generates demand for B/30 of 210 minutes and demand for D/30 of 110 minutes to be completed on resource R-4 8 hours prior to the end of ship date 100. So the load for each is placed at the end of day 99 at hour 8:00.

Sales order S/O222 will be filled by inventory which exists at part/operation F/20. Since this part/operation exists prior to part/operations G/30 and H/30, no demand will be generated.

The next order on the master schedule is S/O333. This order generates 410 minutes on resource R-4 to create part/operation G/30 and 210 minutes to create part/operation H/30.

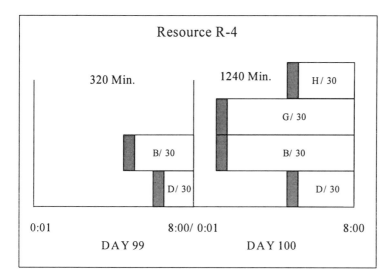

Figure 5.18 Accumulating demand.

The last order generated is to fill a forecast for 20 As on day 101. This places 410 minutes demand on part/operation B/30 and 210 minutes on D/30 at the end of day 100. The total load on resource R-4 is 1240 minutes for day 100 and 320 minutes for day 99.

Pushing the Load Toward Time Zero

The next step in the process, after all resource labor is placed on the time line for every Part/operation, is to level the load. Since the protection exists to the right, the process of leveling the load begins at the end of the planning horizon and moves constantly toward time zero (to the left). The original protection generated at the time the orders were placed on the time line will thus still be available.

Notice that resource R-4 has two machines. This means that two orders, one on each machine, can be run concurrently.

The first Part/operations to be placed are B/30 and D/30 from the forecast (see Figure 5.19). Part/operations B/30 and D/30 were placed so that their completion times were the same as those for the original placement on the time line. There were no additional machines on which to place H/30 and G/30 for

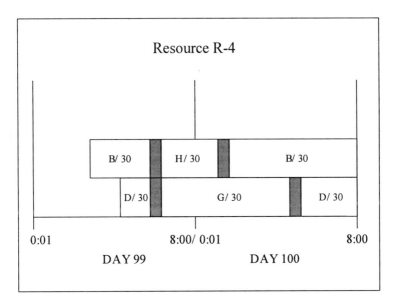

Figure 5.19 Pushing the load toward time zero.

sales order S/O333, so they needed to be moved. Part/operations B/30 and D/30 from sales order S/O111 were repositioned last.

Notice that B/30 and D/30 for sales order S/O111 did not include setup time. Since setup savings can have a very large impact on finding additional capacity, for the purposes of identifying the constraint additional setups are left out. One setup for part/operations B/30 and D/30 had already been placed.

Re-Computing Start and Stop Times

In re-computing start and stop times for G/30 and H/30, they were placed immediately after D/30 and B/30, respectively (see Figure 5.20).

D/30 from the forecast has a start time of hour 4:30 on day 100, so G/30 must stop at 4:31 on day 100. After subtracting the 410 minutes for processing time, G/30's start time is placed at 5:41 on day 99.

B/30's start time is hour 1:10 also on day 100, so H/30 must stop at 1:09 day 100. After subtracting 210 minutes, H/30's start time is computed as 5:39 on day 99.

Sales Order/Qty	Order Due	Part/ Oper.	Proc. Qty	Setup Time	Run Time	Total Time	Start Time	End Time
S/O111/20	100	B/30	20	10	10	210	99/2:18	99/5:38
		D/30	10	10	10	110	99/4:00	99/5:40
S/O222/10	100	G/30		10	10	0		
		H/30		10	10	0		
S/O333/20	101	G/30	40	10	10	410	99/5:41	100/4:31
		H/30	20	10	10	210	99/5:39	100/1:09
Forecast/20	101	B/30	40	10	10	410	100/1:10	100/8:00
		D/30	20	10	10	210	100/4:30	100/8:00

Figure 5.20   Re-computing start and stop times.

Part/operation D/30 for S/O111 is placed after G/30's start time of 5:41 day 99. Its stop time is therefore 5:40 on day 99. After subtracting 100 minutes for processing time, D/30's start time is placed at 4:00. (Notice that the time for the second placement of a D/30 part/operation did not include setup time.)

The last part/operation to be repositioned is B/30. Its stop time is placed immediately after H/30's stop time of 5:39 day 99. Its start time is placed 200 minutes earlier at 2:18 day 99.

Consuming Protective Capacity

To demonstrate the consumption of protective capacity, machine 2 will be removed from resource R-4, cutting its capacity in half. The load requirements will remain the same (see Figure 5.21).

Time zero has been placed at just over halfway through day 98. This happens to coincide with the beginning of the run time portion of part/operation H/30, which means that all the setup time for H/30 and the run time for D/30 as well as B/30 must be run in the past. Obviously, this cannot occur and the orders must be adjusted. But in comparing one resource with another, there must be a number which represents the extent to which each resource has passed time

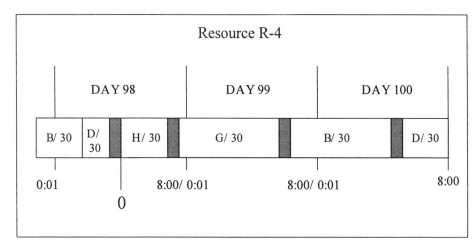

Figure 5.21 Consuming protective capacity.

zero. The time allocated to the orders which have passed time zero must be accumulated. In the case of resource R-4, the load has passed time zero by the setup time for H/30 (10 minutes) plus the run time for D/30 (100 minutes) plus the run time for B/30 (200 minutes) for a total of 310 minutes. This means that R-4's demand has taken 310 minutes of protective capacity away from the system.

Note: while 310 minutes of protective capacity has been taken, the impact to individual orders is still uncertain. This can only be determined after pushing the load so that B/30's start time is equal to time zero.

Re-computing start and stop times for a one-machine scenario

Figure 5.22 is a representation of the new placement of each part/operation for the load on resource R-4. Notice that the start time of B/30 for sales order S/O111 has been set at 5:57 on day 97. Time zero is at hour 3:09 on day 98 and is actually set to the computer's current date and time at the beginning of the process.

Unless there is another resource which pushes demand even farther past time 5:57 on day 97, resource R-4 would be considered the first candidate for the primary constraint.

Sales Order/Qty	Order Due	Part/ Oper.	Proc. Qty	Setup Time	Run Time	Total Time	Start Time	End Time
S/O111/20	100	B/30	20	10	10	210	97/5:57	98/1:27
		D/30	10	10	10	110	98/1:28	98/3:18
S/O222/10	100	G/30		10	10	0		
		H/30		10	10	0		
S/O333/20	101	G/30	40	10	10	410	98/6:50	99/5:40
		H/30	20	10	10	210	98/3:19	98/6:49
Forecast/20	101	B/30	40	10	10	410	99/5:41	100/4:31
		D/30	20	10	10	210	100/4:30	100/8:00

Figure 5.22 Re-computing start and stop times—one-machine example.

In order to ensure that resource R-4 performed to the maximum capable in generating throughput, it must be exploited. This would include generating a schedule to ensure that, if followed, orders would arrive to shipping on time.

CONCLUSION

When trying to identify those resources which have limited capacity to perform to the demands of the market, simply dividing capacity by demand will not accomplish the desired task. Given the physical issues which must be addressed a different approach should be used which assesses the amount of protection required and then applies the demand created by a given master schedule against the protection.

STUDY QUESTIONS

1. What impact do statistical fluctuations have on the generation of a schedule?

2. What role does protective capacity play in the generation of a schedule?

3. What purpose does the shipping buffer serve?

4. When applying demand to the available capacity for a specific schedule generated by the master schedule, what is the traditional method used and why does it fail to accomplish its task?

5. Define what is meant by the term time zero and describe its function.

6. Describe the method used to identify the constraint using the TOC based system.

7. What data elements are needed by the TOC based system to identify the constraint?

8. What data elements are contained in the net?

9. What is meant by the term consuming protective capacity?

10. How does excess capacity manifest itself?

11. What is the purpose of productive capacity?

12. What should the goal of an information system be and why?

Resource R-4

Sales Order/Qty	Order Due	Part/ Oper.	Proc. Qty	Setup Time	Run Time	Total Time	Start Time	End Time
S/O111/20	150	B/30	10	10	15			
		D/30	40	15	10			
S/O333/20	151	G/30	15	20	15			
		H/30	20	10	20			
Forecast/20	151	B/30	20	10	15			
		D/30	40	15	10			

Shipping Buffer = 12 hours

Figure 5.23 Data for study questions 14 and 15.

13. What is meant by the term processing on the net?

14. Using the data in Figure 5.23, compute the start and stop times for the initial placement of orders on the time line.

15. Once the start and stop times have been computed for question 14, level the load, re-computing the start and stop times based on an 8 hour day. Assume only one machine is available. Time zero will be day 147.

6

Exploitation

The purpose of exploitation is to maximize the amount of throughput generated by the constraint. While this can mean a number of different activities, such as insuring that the correct product mix is being sold into the market, for the purposes of this chapter, the exploitation process of scheduling will be the primary subject.

CHAPTER OBJECTIVES

- To address the process of scheduling the constraint
- To demonstrate how the new system identifies possible trouble areas
- To show how to maximize the constraints utilization

EXPLOITATION IN SCHEDULING

In scheduling the constraint, the objective is to maximize its time by insuring that

- It is constantly operating to generate throughput
- Whenever and wherever possible, additional constraint time is found
- Those orders which may have particular problems are identified so that action can be taken

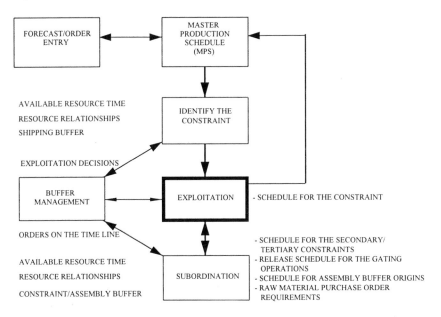

Figure 6.1 The TOC based system—exploitation.

Re-Adjusting Orders on the Time Line

In Chapter 5 resource R-4 had been identified as a candidate for the primary constraint. Since the orders have already been placed on the time line but are attempting to use time which no longer exists, the first step in the exploitation process would be to push the orders so that they are no longer in the past (see Figure 6.2).

By moving the orders so that none appear prior to time zero, all orders on the time line have been shifted to the right. Each order will now have a different start and stop time, which will be in this case 330 minutes later. The 330 minutes was determined by adding the setup time for H/30 (10 minutes) plus the setup and run time for B/30 (210 minutes) plus the setup and run time for D/30 (110 minutes). Notice that the setup times for D/30 and B/30 have been added back to the schedule.

Note: while 310 minutes of protective capacity has been taken from resource R-4, the impact to individual orders is still uncertain. This can only be determined

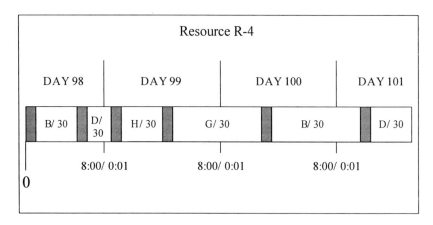

Figure 6.2   Adjusting orders on the time line.

after pushing the load so that B/30's start time is equal to time zero. A comparison can then be made between the stop date and time of the individual order and the due date and time of the sales order to the length of shipping buffer.

Re-computing start and stop times

As mentioned, the new start date and times can be determined by adding 330 minutes to the start and end dates and times for each part/operation of resource R-4 (see Figure 6.3).

Analyzing the impact to each order

In re-computing the start and stop times for each order, each must be compared to the original placement to determine the true impact to the protection allocated to each order (see Figure 6.4).

Notice that B/30's total buffer is 14 hours and 57 minutes and is over the requirement of 8 hours by 6 hours and 57 minutes. D/30 also has an excess in buffer time of 7 hours 17 minutes. This means that S/O111 will have no problems in meeting its due date requirements.

S/O333 should also have no problems in meeting its due date. However, the forecast of 20 part As is in jeopardy. While part/operation B/30 still has over 50% of its buffer remaining and should be on time, it must be matched with

Sales Order/Qty	Order Due	Part/ Oper.	Proc. Qty	Setup Time	Run Time	Total Time	Start Time	End Time
S/O111/20	100	B/30	20	10	10	210	98/3:27	98/6:57
		D/30	10	10	10	110	98/6:58	99/0:48
S/O222/10	100	G/30		10	10	0		
		H/30		10	10	0		
S/O333/20	101	G/30	40	10	10	410	99/6:20	100/3:50
		H/30	20	10	10	210	99/0:49	99/6:19
Forecast/20	101	B/30	40	10	10	410	100:/3:51	101/2:01
		D/30	20	10	10	210	101/2:02	101/5:32

Figure 6.3 Re-computing start and stop times.

Sales Order/Qty	Order Due	Part/ Oper.	Buffer Due	End Time	Buffer Avail.	Buffer Req. l	Delta
S/O111/20	100	B/30	99/8:00	98/6:57	14:57	8 hours	+6:57
		D/30	99/8:00	99/0:48	15:17	8 hours	+7:17
S/O222/10	100	G/30					
		H/30					
S/O333/20	101	G/30	100/8:00	100/3:50	12:19	8 hours	+4:19
		H/30	100/8:00	99/6:19	14:19	8 hours	+6:19
Forecast/20	101	B/30	100/8:00	101/2:01	5:59	8 hours	-2:01
		D/30	100/8:00	101/5:32	2:28	8 hours	-5:32

Figure 6.4 Analyzing the impact to the protection allocated to each order.

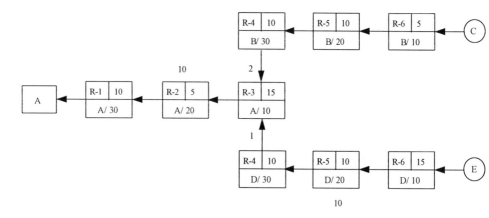

Figure 6.5 Adjusting for inventory—the net.

part/operation D/30. Part/operation D/30 has only 2 hours and 28 minutes, or 34% of its original protection, available. The probability of D/30 completing on time is extremely low due to the lack of adequate protection. The forecast of 20 product As will be late.

Adjusting for inventory

Notice that only one of the part/operations (D/30) scheduled to cross R-4 has inventory available to begin processing on the portion of the net for product A (Figure 6.5). But B/30 is scheduled first. This means that if resource R-4 were to be the primary constraint throughput, would drop immediately unless the schedule were changed to process part/operation D/30 first.

Since no other part/operations for any other resource have been scheduled there will not be a product mix problem. Other resource requirements must be determined by the demand created by the constraint, and unless a finalized schedule has been created, product mix is not an issue at this time (see Figure 6.6).

Notice that D/30 for sales order S/O111 is now scheduled to be run on resource R-4 first. The resulting changes to the start and stop times are effected for D/30 and B/30 only (see Figure 6.7). The previous example isolated one order with material to move to the front of the schedule. To ensure that the constraint is

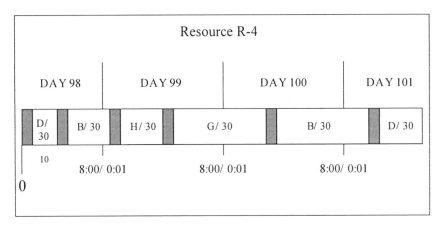

Figure 6.6 Adjusting for inventory—resource R-4.

protected in reality, enough orders with material should be in front of the constraint to cover two-thirds the length of the constraint buffer.

Exploiting the Constraint Through Setup Savings

There are a number of ways in which D/30's problem can be fixed. One is the possibility that by combining the orders for D/30 and B/30 from the forecast with those from sales order S/O111 additional time can be found by saving setup. The key issue here is to ensure that no other problems will be created in the process.

Sales Order/Qty	Order Due	Part/ Oper.	Proc. Qty	Setup Time	Run Time	Total Time	Start Time	End Time
S/O111/20	100	D/30	10	10	10	110	98/3:27	98/5:17
		B/30	20	10	10	210	98/5:18	99/0:48

Figure 6.7 Adjusting start and stop times.

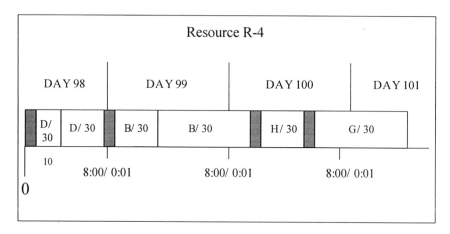

Figure 6.8   The impact of setup savings.

Since there is only 20 minutes of setup time that can be gained and the amount of buffer that has been taken by the schedule for part/operation D/30 is 5 hours and 32 minutes it seems unlikely that a solution can be found. However, Figure 6.8 shows the impact of setup savings.

Notice that B/30 and D/30 from the forecast have been combined with D/30 and B/30 from S/O111 to save setup. Notice also that G/30 and H/30 have been pushed out to later dates by the amount of displacement caused by the run times for the forecasted D/30 and B/30 part/operations (see Figure 6.9).

The completion time for G/30 is now set at 101/5:12 and 20 minutes of constraint time has been saved, which can be used to create other products. However, the lateness of order S/O333 may be a problem for the customer. Unless the customer can live with the order being late it may be best not to use setup savings. In addition, the forecast has yet to be sold. Processing it instead of products that can generate immediate throughput is not the wisest choice.

Setup savings can involve a number of issues. If the size of individual setups is large or the number of setups within the planning horizon is high, then setup savings can be a great way of gaining additional constraint time. However, in setup savings it is important to remember that whenever two orders are combined, another orders start date is postponed.

Sales Order/Qty	Order Due	Part/ Oper.	Proc. Qty	Setup Time	Run Time	Total Time	Start Time	End Time
S/O111/20	100	D/30	10	10	10	110	98/3:27	98/5:17
Forecast/20	101	D/30	20	10	10	200	98/5:18	99/0:38
S/O111/20	100	B/30	20	10	10	210	99/0:39	99/4:09
Forecast/20	101	B/30	40	10	10	400	99/4:10	100/2:50
S/O222/10	100	G/30		10	10	0		
		H/30		10	10	0		
S/O333/20	101	G/30	40	10	10	410	100/6:22	101/5:12
		H/30	20	10	10	210	100/2:51	100/6:21

Figure 6.9 Computing start and stop times for setup savings.

The impact of setup savings on other resources

Setup savings can have a positive or negative impact on any given resource. Once setup savings has been performed, those resources which exist prior to scheduled resource must perform to the new demand created by setup savings. This may not be good for those resources already approaching constraint levels.

Figure 6.10 represents a chain of resources starting with resource 1 on the left. Each resource feeds the next in succession until finally reaching resource number 4. The capacity of resource 4 is 50 units per hour and is loaded to 100%.

Figure 6.10 The impact of setup savings.

When setup savings is performed as in Figure 6.8, more units can be produced in less time. Some of the capacity that was dedicated to performing setup activity will now be dedicated to productive activity.

Notice that resource 3 is loaded to 90% when resource 4 is producing at 50 units per hour. What will be the impact on resource 3 if, through setup savings, resource 4 now produces 60 units per hour? The demand on resource 3 will increase. Since it is already loaded to 90% of its rated capacity, resource 3 will probably become a secondary constraint. As a result, a schedule must be built for resource 3 maximizing its utilization so that 4's new production rate can be protected. Along with the creation of the schedule a buffer must also be created. An additional buffer means an increase in inventory in front of the secondary constraint.

The situation as described above is not necessarily bad. Remember that because resource 4 is now producing more, additional throughput is being generated to offset the additional inventory. The real problem is created if resource 3 cannot be subordinated to the schedule created on resource 4.

Limiting the extent of setup savings

If for every order that is pulled in and combined other orders are displaced, then it may be wise to limit the number of orders which can be combined. As an example, in Figure 6.11, the top grouping of orders represents the schedule prior to setup savings. In the second grouping three As are combined, one from the beginning, one from the middle and one from the end of the original schedule. The amount of time saved was approximately equal to the amount of setup and run time for one A. However, notice how far to the right the first C has been moved. Its position is now close to the end of the schedule.

The questions that must be asked during setup savings are

- How far into the schedule should the process go?
- Should there be a limitation?
- If so, what should the limitation be?

One method discussed in *The Haystack Syndrome* is to use a number which can relate the amount of setup saved with the amount of time into the future to look for additional orders. As an example, the number 25 would mean that for every hour saved the system might look into the future by 25 hours. As seen in Figure 6.11 it is important to limit the amount of setup savings which can be used in the planning horizon to some adjustable number (see Figure 6.12).

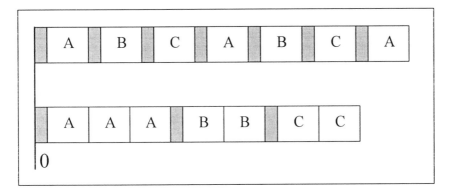

Figure 6.11 Setup savings.

Notice that the last A in the schedule was not pulled in to be combined with the order for the first and second A. Instead, only two As were combined. Notice also that the first order of C was not pushed out as far.

Note: one rule to remember in executing setup savings is not to make matters worse than they already are.

Looping Back to the MPS

Since a decision has been made not to perform setup savings and the forecast for product A is going to be late, when should the MPS be told to expect this

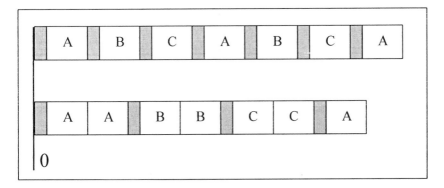

Figure 6.12 Limiting the amount of setup savings.

Resource R-4

Forecast/20	101	B/30	40	10	10	410	100:/3:11	101/2:01
		D/30	20	10	10	210	101/2:02	101/5:32

Part Operation Due + Shipping buffer = New Delivery Date/Time

$$101/5:32 + 8 = \mathbf{102/5:32}$$

Figure 6.l3   Looping back to the MPS.

product to be available to promise (ATP) (if forecasted) or shipped (if a sales order)?

Once an actual due date for the part/operation has been established for the constraint, it is the due date plus the shipping buffer which establishes the new date (see Figure 6.13). The master schedule would be instructed to re-schedule the forecast for 20 As from 101/5:32 (the due date of the order across the constraint) to 102/5:32 (the constraint's due date plus the 8 hour buffer).

Identifying Late Orders

Sales orders are considered to be having serious timing problems whenever the due date of the order crossing the constraint uses over 50% of the buffer in front of shipping. In other words, if the due date of the order is greater that the ship date of the sales order minus one-half the shipping buffer, it will be late.

Whenever the buffer is being used at less than 50% but more than zero it is considered a potential problem, but no action is usually taken.

Late orders list

The late orders list is a feature of the system and shows those orders which are going to be late according to their original due dates and how many days they will be late (see Figure 6.14).

Part/Op.	Qty	Sales Orders	Sales Qty	Due	Days Late
A/30	100	S/O111	50	152	2
		S/O222	50	153	1
B/30	150	S/O333	150	154	5
B/30	50	S/O111	50	154	5

Figure 6.14 The late orders list.

Applying Overtime

The way overtime is applied can have three effects:

- If begun too early in the process, it will drive inventory up.
- If begun too late in the process, it will increase operating expense without maximizing the throughput generated.
- If done at the right time and place, inventory and operating expense can be held to a minimum while maximizing the amount of throughput generated.

Any time a part/operation will be late overtime is a valid option, but only after all attempts have been made to gain more capacity (as in setup savings) without spending more money. In attempting to maximize throughput at the constraint prior to spending overtime, the constraint may be sufficiently exploited and overtime may not be needed. Whenever authorized, overtime should be used sparingly and only at the right time and place.

It's not enough to know that the schedule is late. Specifically if it can be fixed. When and where to place overtime and what orders are being threatened are major concerns. If it is possible to pinpoint exactly when overtime should be worked, what resources are involved, and what part/operations are to receive the overtime effort, then applying the additional expense will have a direct effect on increasing throughput while keeping inventory and operating expense to only that required.

In Figure 6.15. the two shaded orders, 3 and 6, are indicating that they are using over 50% of the buffer and that they will be late unless something is done. All

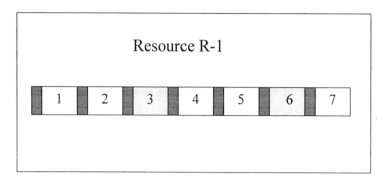

Figure 6.15 Overtime decision-making.

attempts so far to gain additional capacity have failed to solve this problem, so overtime is suggested. The question left unanswered is where must the overtime be applied to maximize effectiveness.

The closer to time zero that overtime is applied, the greater the number of orders it will affect. As an example, if overtime were applied to order 1 above, it would impact the due date of every order in the schedule by completing them earlier. It would also require that more inventory be made available for processing.

If overtime were applied to order 7, it would impact only order 7. The amount of additional throughput generated would therefore be minimized. If overtime were applied to order 2, inventory would be held to the minimum required, while throughput would be maximized in that all orders to the right of order 2 would be impacted favorably. It is only after expending all allowable overtime on order 2 and still showing late orders that order 1 be allowed to absorb additional over time.

If the scheduling problem still persists, the next 2 hour block of overtime would be applied to order 5, followed by an equal amount applied to order 4. This process of jumping forward to add overtime to the order just in front of the late order continues until one of the following occurs:

- All late orders have been fixed
- All available overtime has been expended
- The end of the planning horizon is reached

There is an important exception to this process. Overtime is usually spent at the end of the day. If order 2 existed in the same day as order 3, then the overtime would come too late. It would be expended at the end of the day, and since order 3 comes after order 2 the overtime would be placed after order 3 begins and ends. This means that no change will be made in order 3's timing.

So there must be a modification to the rule. Overtime must be placed at the end of the day prior to the late order and should be expended first on those orders which are closest in time, but exist prior to, the late order.

Limiting the amount of overtime

Overtime is usually limited in the system based on the amount of overtime to be applied per day or week. If overtime were limited to 2 hours but this was not enough to make orders 3 and 6 finish on time, then more overtime must be spent. Two hours was originally spent on order 2. Since this did not solve the problem, an additional 2 hours could be applied to order 1.

Re-Computing Start and Stop Times

The original schedule for D/30 in the forecast placed it 5 hours and 32 minutes into the 8 hour buffer (see Figure 6.16). In order to solve this problem, 2 hours of overtime is applied at the end of day 100 to part/operation B/30 (see Figure 6.17).

Notice that part/operation B/30 now finishes 2 hours earlier allowing D/30 to start and finish earlier. Since D/30 now finishes at 101/3:32, it uses less of the buffer (44%) and should reach shipping on time. No additional overtime is required. Notice, however, that this order is marginal. If a large percentage of

Sales Order/Qty	Order Due	Part/ Oper.	Proc. Qty	Setup Time	Run Time	Total Time	Start Time	End Time
Forecast/20	101	B/30	40	10	10	410	100:/3:11	101/2:01
		D/30	20	10	10	210	101/2:02	101/5:32

Figure 6.16 Re-computing start and stop times.

Sales Order/Qty	Order Due	Part/ Oper.	Proc. Qty	Setup Time	Run Time	Total Time	Start Time	End Time
Forecast/20	101	B/30	40	10	10	410	100:/3:11	101/0:01
		D/30	20	10	10	210	101/0:02	101/3:32

Figure 6.17   Placing the overtime.

orders will use buffer time while generating the schedule, the cumulative effect can have a negative impact to on-time delivery.

Manual overtime assignment

While the system should provide the ability to automatically add overtime to the appropriate resource, it will be advantageous to also provide the ability to apply additional overtime manually. When reviewing orders on the time line the system should provide the ability to select specific orders on which to spend the additional overtime.

Off-Loading

If the attempt to gain more capacity through setup savings fails, it might be a good idea to off-load an order to another resource which is capable of handling it (see Figure 6.18).

Schedule A for resource R-4 indicates that orders 3 and 6 are late. Notice that order number 2 is no longer on schedule B and that orders 3 and 6 are now on time as indicated by the shading being removed. Order 2 was chosen because it was early in the process and, as discussed, will impact a majority of orders. When choosing an order to off-load keep in mind that the object of the exercise is to improve the situation, not cause more problems. Choose an order, or a number of orders, which exists early in the schedule, approximately equals the total amount of late buffer minutes, and for which there is another resource that will not be negatively affected.

While it is not always possible to find additional capacity by off-loading to a different resource, it can be a very effective alternative. However, the only way

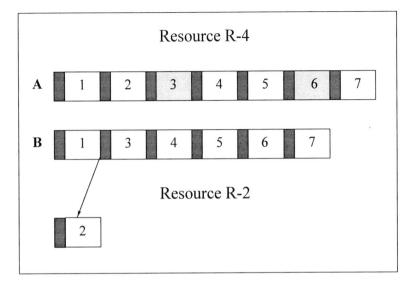

Figure 6.18 Off-loading to alternative resources.

to understand the impact of an order which has been off-loaded is through attempting to subordinate the resource on which the order is now being processed with the schedule currently being created for the primary constraint. It may be found that it is impossible to schedule the remaining resources to the additional capacity generated by the off-load (see Figure 6.19).

Resource 4 is loaded to 120% and is the primary constraint. Scheduling and setup savings have not been able to reduce the load adequately. A decision has been made to off-load orders from resource 4 to another resource. The only resource capable of handling the requirements demanded to create the part is

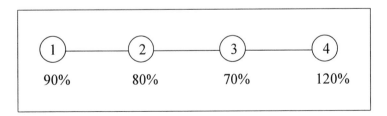

Figure 6.19 The impact of off-loading on the subordination process.

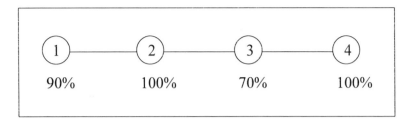

Figure 6.20   The impact of off-loading on the subordination process—situation after orders from resource 4 off-loaded to resource 2.

resource 2, which is loaded to 80%. When the load is taken from resource 4 and placed on resource 2 the demand for resource 2 increases to 100% (see Figure 6.20).

This means that the string of resources needed to produce the product has three resources in the chain of four which are over 90%, and two are loaded to 100%. The chance of being successful with resources scheduled to this extent seems remote. However, to ensure that off-loading from resource 4 to resource 2 is viable will require creating a secondary schedule for resource 2. If any conflicts exist between the schedules, then off-loading to resource 2 will probably not be a good alternative.

Lot splitting

During the off-loading process it may be desirable to off-load less than an entire batch. It may be that in off-loading less than the entire amount the user is able to prevent problems occurring while attempting to subordinate to the constraints schedule (see Figure 6.21).

Notice that order 2 now appears on both resource R-4 and R-2 and that setup times exist for both lots. While the total time for processing order 2 will increase, if resource R-2 has enough capacity, then throughput will go up and there will be no impact to inventory or operating expense.

PROBLEMS WHEN THE CONSTRAINT FEEDS ITSELF

Often there exists a problem where an order which must be processed on the constraint at one part/operation must be processed again at a later part/operation.

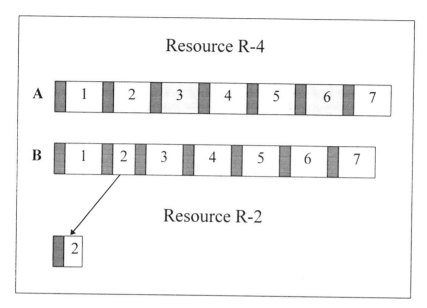

Figure 6.21 Lot splitting.

This order actually appears on the schedule for the constraint in two places, once for the earlier part/operation and again for the second.

If an order is to appear in two places on the same schedule, there must be time allotted for the order to be processed at the first part/operation, continue to other resources and then return. But remember that when each order was placed on the constraint an estimate of the time buffer needed was applied equally to all orders. Unless something is done to change this, both part/operations will be scheduled to cross the constraint, at least initially, at the same time. When the load is leveled this will change, but there is no guarantee that the part/operations will not appear next to each other on the constraint schedule. This is a problem. There must be a mechanism to ensure that when an order has two part/operations which cross the constraint that they appear in the correct sequence and that they are kept a minimum distance from each other (see Figure 6.22).

In schedule A, part/operations 3 and 4 belong to the same sales order. Each must be processed on the constraint, but after 3 is processed it must leave the constraint to receive processing at other resources and then return as part/

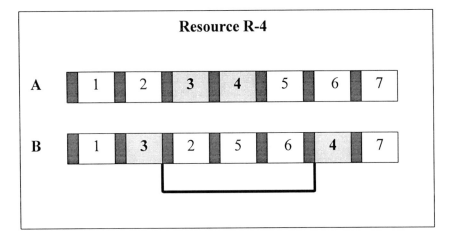

Figure 6.22   Orders 3 and 4 must be held apart to keep them from appearing adjacent on the constraint's schedule.

operation 4. Since the stop time for 3 is almost identical with the start time for 4, the likelihood of having the necessary procedures completed are nil.

What is needed is some kind of a buffering mechanism which will ensure that these part/operations do not appear too close together within the schedule for the constraint (see schedule B). Notice that 3 and 4 have a certain amount of protection, which has been applied to them so that they do not appear together on the constraint's schedule.

Rods

Rods, initially introduced in *The Haystack Syndrome*, is the term given to the buffering mechanism briefly discussed in the last section. There are two situations in which rods become necessary:

- Whenever there is a connection between part/operations on the same resource schedule, as seen in Figure 6.22
- Whenever a connection exists between the schedule of part/operations on multiple resources

There are also a number of different types:

- Forward rods
- Backward rods
- Combination rods

Forward rods are used to keep part/operations from advancing too far forward and extend from the front of one part/operation on the schedule to the back of the next one. Backward rods extend from the back of a part/operation to the front of a preceding part/operation. Combination rods do both.

There can be opportunities for many conflicts requiring this kind of resolution within the same or multiple schedules. However, what will be discussed here will be those conflicts and the rods which apply to a single schedule. Multiple schedule conflicts will be discussed during Chapter 7, "Subordination."

Forward rods

Figure 6.23 represents two forward rods. Notice that there are two rods extending from part/operation A to part/operation B. The objective is to ensure that when these two part/operations are placed on the time line and during the subsequent scheduling process that the first part finished at part/operation A will be completed a minimum amount of time from the start of the first part at part/operation B. Additionally, the last part at A should finish at minimal time before the last part at B begins.

Figure 6.23 Forward rods.

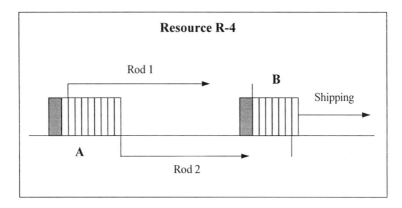

Figure 6.24 Forward rods—B may be shifted to the right only.

It is not necessary that A finish exactly X distance from B. It may finish earlier (see Figure 6.24). But, it should never finish less than X distance. In the order of initial placement, B would be placed on the time line first based on the shipping buffer and, since A must finish before B, it should be placed a minimum of one-half the constraint buffer in the direction of time zero. When the orders are leveled during the identification process, A might be pushed further away from B. It should never be moved closer.

Computing the length of the rods

Obviously, the rods are a simple method of describing the buffering activity graphically and do not exist inside the computer in anything more than mathematical computations (see Figure 6.25).

The length of one-half the constraint buffer is 240 minutes. Setup time is 20 minutes for both part/operations and run time is 10 minutes per piece. Each of the small non-striped blocks represents a part. To compute rod 1 the amount of run time for all but the first part of part/operation A (110 minutes) is added to the length of the buffer (240 minutes) plus the setup for part/operation B (20 minutes). The length of rod 1 is 370 minutes.

Rod 2 is computed as the length of the buffer (240 minutes) added to the setup time for part/operation B (20 minutes) plus the run time for all but the last part. The length of rod 2 is 300 minutes.

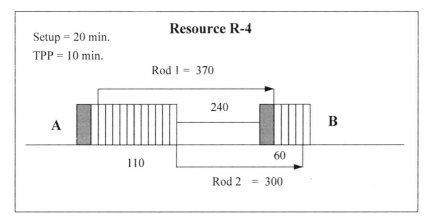

Figure 6.25 Computing the length of the forward rods.

Backward rods

Backward rods move from the latest part/operation to the earliest. Notice in Figure 6.26 that rod 1 originates at the end of setup for B and stops at the stop time for the first part for A. Rod 2 starts at the beginning of the last part B and stops at the end of the last part A. The objective here is that if B must move to the left, it will push part/operation A into an earlier time (to the left).

Figure 6.26 Backward rods.

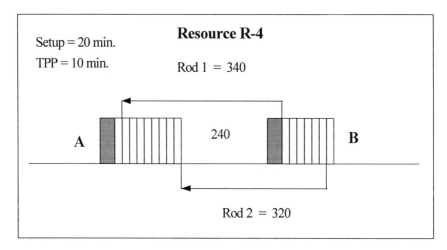

Figure 6.27   Computing the length of the backward rods.

The length of the backward rods are computed similar to the forward rods. Rod 1 equals the setup time for B (20 minutes) plus the buffer (240 minutes) plus the run time for all but the first part A (80 minutes), or 320 minutes (see Figure 6.27).

Rod 2 equals the run time for all but the last B (60 minutes) plus B's setup time (20 minutes) plus the buffer (240 minutes), or 320 minutes.

Combination rods

Combination rods extend both forwards and backwards. The length of the rods are computed the same as in figures 6.25 and 6.27 for each of the other rod types (see Figure 6.28).

The objective of the combination rods is to ensure that if A were to move to the right B and C would also move. If C were moved to the left A and B would move. In a complex environment there may be many orders attached in sequence.

The effect of the rods on setup savings

As explained, the purpose of the rods is to maintain minimal distance between specific part/operations during the scheduling process. Part/operations 3 and 6

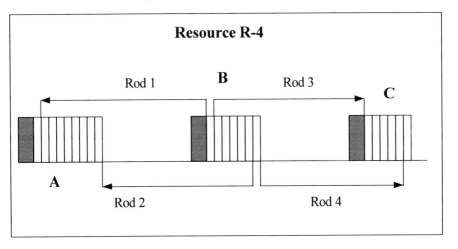

Figure 6.28 Combination rods.

are scheduled on the constraint. 3 is an earlier part/operation which feeds 6. In Figure 6.29 a decision has been made to perform setup savings by combining two similar part/operations with the same setup (2 and 4). Normally during setup savings the later part is moved forward and combined with the earlier part.

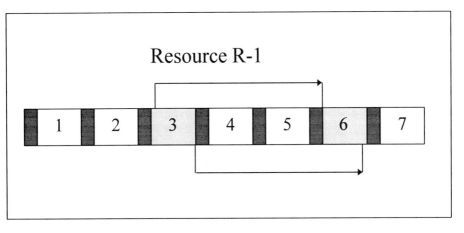

Figure 6.29 The impact of rods on setup savings.

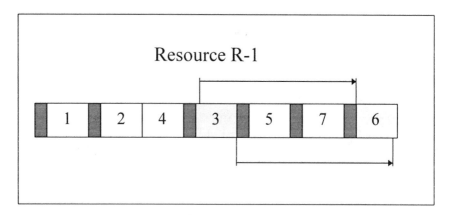

Figure 6.30   The impact of rods on setup savings—since 3 was pushed into the future, 6 had to be also.

In Figure 6.30 when bringing 4 forward, 3 was pushed into the future. However, that is also the direction of part/operation 6. Since 3 was pushed into the future, 6 was also pushed to maintain the minimum distance prescribed by the rods. Notice also that 7 took 6's position on the schedule.

Re-Computing Start and Stop Times

Figure 6.31 represents the constraint schedule and some detail information for R-4. F/30 and A/10 belong to sales order A for a quantity of 10 pieces. Since F/30 feeds A/10 and appears on the same schedule, rods have been created. Notice that F/30 has a pair of forward rods under the headings R-1 and R-2.

Forward rod 1 extends 340 minutes from the end of the run time of the first part F/30 toward part A/10. Forward rod 2 extends 385 minutes from the end of F/30 to the beginning of the last part A/10. A/10 has a pair of rods which extend toward F/30.

During the scheduling process, which starts with F/30 and ends with E/30, the forward rods from F/30 were used to push A/10 into a different time slot. Rod one extends from 3:47 of day 98 (the time was computed as hour 3:27 plus setup of 10 minutes plus the 10 minutes run time for one part) until 1:27 of

Resource R-4

Sales Order/Qty	Part/ Oper.	Proc. Qty	Setup Time	Run Time	Total Time	Start Time	End Time		R1	R2
S/O-A/10	F/30	10	10	10	110	98/3:27	98/5:17	F	340	385
	A/10	10	10	15	160	99/1:17	99/3:57	B	340	385
S/O-B/10	B/20	10	10	10	110	98/5:18	98/7:08			
S/O-C/20	C/30	20	10	10	210	99/3:58	99/7:28			
S/O-D/10	D/10	10	10	10	110	99/7:29	100/1:19			
S/O-E/20	E/30	20	10	10	210	100/1:20	100/4:50			

Constrain Buffer = 480 minutes

Figure 6.31 Re-computing start and stop times maintaining the rods.

day 99. Minus the setup time for A/10 of ten minutes, this places A/10's start time at 1:17.

B/20 was scheduled to start immediately following F/30. Notice that C/30 is scheduled to start at 3:58, immediately following A/10.

The scheduling of A/10 at the end of the rod has caused a 2 hour and 9 minute hole to develop in the schedule from day 98 at 7:08 to day 99 at 1:17.

The easiest way to solve the problem is to delay the scheduling of A/10 until immediately after C/30 on day 99 (see Figure 6.32). A/10, because of the rods, can be scheduled further away but not closer to F/30.

SUMMARY

It is the schedule of the constraint which establishes the rate at which throughput enters the company. If the constraint is able to process more orders, then the

Resource R-4

Sales Order/Qty	Part/ Oper.	Proc. Qty	Setup Time	Run Time	Total Time	Start Time	End Time		R1	R2
S/O-A/10	F/30	10	10	10	110	98/3:27	98/5:17	F	340	385
	A/10	10	10	15	160	99/2:40	99/5:20	B	340	385
S/O-B/10	B/20	10	10	10	110	98/5:18	98/7:08			
S/O-C/20	C/30	20	10	10	210	98/7:09	99/2:39			
S/O-D/10	D/10	10	10	10	110	99/5:21	99/7:11			
S/O-E/20	E/30	20	10	10	210	99/7:11	100/2:41			

Constrain Buffer = 480 minutes

Figure 6.32 Computing start and stop times maintaining the rods.

amount of money the company makes is maximized. The exploitation phase is designed to enhance that effort and means a tremendous difference in how resources should be scheduled.

STUDY QUESTIONS

1. List at least five ways of increasing productive capacity on the constraint.

2. Using the output from question 12 at the end of Chapter 5, re-compute the start and stop times of all orders by adjusting for time zero.

3. Define the concept of rods, name each type and show an example of how they are used.

4. How are orders in the schedule for the constraint recognized as having a problem with being delivered on time?

5. What are the rules involved with overtime assignment and what method is used to limit the amount of overtime applied?

6. Apply setup savings, re-computing the start and stop times, to the output of question 1 and define the recommended method of limiting the amount orders being combined within the horizon.

7. Explain the impact of rods on the setup savings process.

7

Subordination

The objective of the subordination phase is to coordinate the activity of all other resources within the factory to ensure that the schedule established for the constraint is protected, that shipping is completed on time and that raw material is released to the floor in synchronization with the way in which it will be consumed. It is an extremely important step in the process.

CHAPTER OBJECTIVES

- To define the subordination process
- To explain the methodology for the creation of secondary/tertiary schedules
- To present methods for resolving schedule conflict
- To define the process for scheduling the release of raw material

THE SUBORDINATION PROCESS

Once the schedule has been created by the exploitation process, it is the subordination phase which defines the activities of all other resources by insuring that certain areas of the factory are provided with what they need (Figure 7.1). It adds a dynamic quality to the system by performing the following functions:

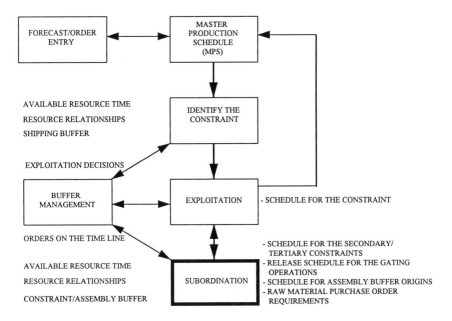

Figure 7.1 The TOC based system—subordination.

- Determining whether there is enough protective capacity on the non-constraints to protect the schedule and automatically increasing the size of the buffer for those buffer origins needing additional capacity
- Identifying those resources for which protective capacity is inadequate (secondary/tertiary constraints) and which threaten the schedule of the primary constraint
- Exploiting those resources identified as additional physical constraints to maximize their ability to deliver to the primary constraint
- Ensuring that there are no conflicts between the schedule created on the primary constraint and the schedule created for the additional constraints
- Preparing the release schedule for raw material into the gating operations and synchronizing the activities of the non-constraints

ESTABLISHING THE BUFFER SYSTEM

The heart of the subordination process is called the buffering system. Since it is the buffer that is used to guide the instructions given to the remaining resources, it literally defines how the subordination process is to be executed. Its role is to ensure that each buffer origin (the area of the factory being protected) is protected from disturbances in the system.

Buffers are established based on those physical laws which govern the manufacturing environment. There are three types. Each serves the purpose of protecting certain areas of the factory from those things which will inevitably happen and cause the creation of throughput to be threatened. Those buffers include:

- The *shipping buffer* is used to protect the shipping of finished goods, to determine the initial schedule for the constraint and to establish the release schedule for raw material which does not go through the constraint or assembly buffer
- The *constraint buffer* is used to protect the constraint(s) and to determine the release of raw material to those operations which feed the constraint.
- The *assembly buffer* is used to ensure that those assembly operations directly fed by the constraint do not wait for material to arrive from non-constrained legs within the net. It also determines the release schedule for raw material into those operations which feed the assembly buffer.

It is the buffering system which synchronizes the way material flows through the factory with the way in which it is consumed and determines the release schedule for raw material. In doing so it serves to protect the creation of throughput (see Figure 7.2).

Each buffer is marked by a rectangular block which designates those resources which are included in the buffer process defined in bold print. Notice that the shipping buffer protects those resources which feed shipping and, in this case, is 8 hours long. The constraint buffer protects resource R-8, which has been determined to be the constraint and is also 8 hours long. Finally, the assembly buffer protects R-2 and is 9 hours long.

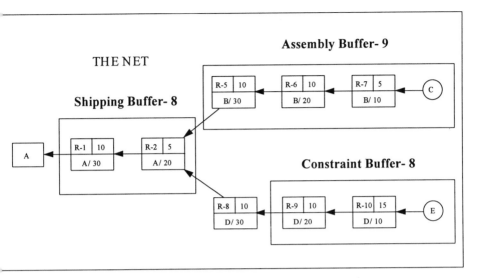

Figure 7.2 Establishing the buffer system.

The release date for raw material C is computed as the sales order due date minus the shipping buffer minus the assembly buffer. If A is due on day 100 at hour 8:00 (assuming an 8 hour day), then C should be released at day 98 hour 7:00. The due date for raw material E is the start date of the order across the constraint minus the constraint buffer. Raw material E should be released to the floor at day 98 hour 8:00. For those raw material items which do not go through the constraint or assembly buffers, the ship date minus the shipping buffer is used.

Material is scheduled in the buffer system by the demand placed on the buffer origin. If a sales order is due by a specific date, then the due date establishes the demand placed on the buffer. The schedule of the constraint causes its demand to be executed within its buffer. The same rule applies to the assembly buffer.

The actual length of the buffer will vary depending on the environment and characteristics of the resources involved. Buffers shrink or grow based on the output of the buffer management system. If material arriving at the buffer origin is consistently late, then the buffer is increased. If it arrives consistently early, then the buffer size is decreased.

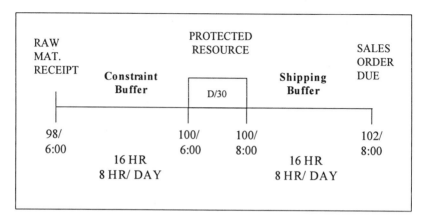

Figure 7.3 Buffering the constraint.

Buffering the Constraint

It is very important to ensure that the constraint, like shipping, is protected from those things which can and will go wrong. The constraint buffer synchronizes that portion of the factory existing in front of the constraint with the constraints schedule. It also determines the release schedule for the gating operations which will eventually feed the constraint (see Figure 7.3).

The sales order is due on day 102 at hour 8:00. There is a 16 hour buffer between the due date of the sales order and the completion of part/operation B/30 on the constraint. So B/30 must be completed by day 100 hour 8:00. Setup and processing require 2 hours. Consequently, B/30 must start at day 100 hour 6:00. The amount of protection for the constraint is estimated to be 16 hours as well. The release of raw material to the gating operation comes at day 98 hour 6:00.

Because of the constraint buffer, raw material will be released at a specific distance in front of the constraint to ensure that, despite any unforeseen problems, the parts will reach the constraint before the constraint is scheduled to consume them.

Remember that the schedule for the constraint may modify the release schedule for raw material. Had D/30 been scheduled at an earlier time during the exploitation process, then the release of raw material would have been offset by the constraint buffer from the earlier start date and time.

Figure 7.4 The assembly buffer.

Assembly Buffers

Assembly buffers are used on those sections of the net that may not be constrained but feed assembly operations which are. They work exactly as constraint or shipping buffers. Notice that the scheduled start date of A/20 from figure 7.4 is used to offset for the release of raw material. A/20 is an assembly operation with at least one leg being fed by the constraint.

DYNAMIC BUFFERING

The heart of the subordination process for the information system *is dynamic buffering.* Dynamic buffering is a process which increases the size of the buffer whenever a lack of adequate protective capacity is detected by the system. If a resource load threatens the ability to deliver to the constraint on time, then the release of raw material is automatically pushed into an earlier time period. It is this feature which adds greatly to the effectiveness of the manual drum-buffer-rope (DBR) process described in *Synchronous Manufacturing* (1990) and in *The Next Phase of Total Quality Management* (1994).

Buffer requirements can be separated into fixed and variable types. The fixed buffer is that portion of the system's buffer which will handle most of the disturbances created by the variation in the ability of resources to perform. The variable buffer is that portion of the buffer which increases or decreases depending on the impact of demand on the schedule. If the demand for a given period of time is greater than the capacity of a resource to handle, it pushes the demand into an earlier period. Pushed far enough, it extends the size of the buffer.

The advent of dynamic buffering has added a great deal to the entire buffering process. By increasing the size of the buffer in only those places and times where it is absolutely necessary, the size of the fixed portion of the buffer can be reduced considerably. Since it is the buffer which determines the release time for raw material, there is a direct effect on the amount of inventory now required to offset for disturbances in the system. Rather than having a large buffer and the corresponding inventory which supports it, inventory will only be increased in those areas where additional protection is absolutely required. The size of the fixed portion of the buffer can be reduced.

Estimating the Load on the System

The first step in dynamic buffering is to develop an estimation of the load on the non-constraints given the schedule for the primary constraint plus the demands created by the master production schedule. To do this means to first allocate inventory which already exists in the system and then compute the load. Allocating inventory in the subordination process, like identification, is done on a first come, first serve basis. Since inventory availability has already been determined between shipping and the constraint, the allocation process must focus on those resources which occur after the constraint (see Figure 7.5). The 10 parts at part/operations H/20 and G/10 must be allocated to orders during processing.

Once the allocation of inventory has been completed, an estimation is made on the amount of capacity required by the non-constraints in order to meet the demand created at the buffer origins. This task is done in much the same fashion as the initial placement of the load for identifying the constraint. The actual resource demand is placed at the end of the buffer and is not leveled. The initial task is to compare capacity with demand as in traditional capacity requirements planning (CRP) (see Figure 7.6). That resource which has, on average, the highest demand compared to capacity requires additional scrutiny.

Resolving peak load problems

Non-constraints by definition have enough capacity, on average, to manage the demand which has been placed on them. However, there will be times when that demand is temporarily greater than the available capacity (see Figure 7.7).

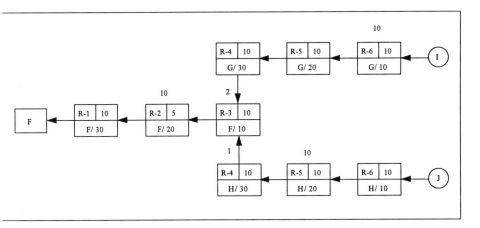

Figure 7.5 Allocating inventory.

The fixed buffer for the constraint places the release date of raw material at the beginning of period 2. However, resource R-5 suffers from a temporary overload in periods 4 and 5. R-5's capacity is placed at 100 hours per day. Period 5 has 25 hours of demand which cannot be met on that day while period 4 has 10 hours. Periods 2 and 3 each have 90 hours of demand so additional time is available for those periods.

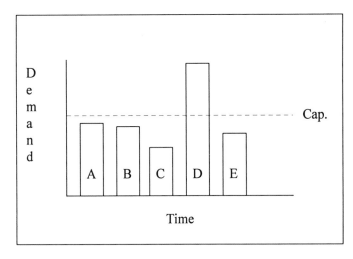

Figure 7.6 Capacity requirements planning.

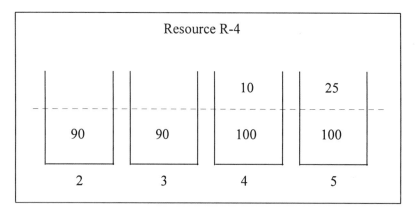

Figure 7.7   Resolving the peak load.

As seen earlier, if the demand on a resource exceeds capacity, the only direction in which to place the load is to an earlier time period. When this occurs on an occasional basis the fixed buffer is capable of managing the impact with little negative effect. However, if there is enough of a load, it can force the normal release time of raw material to be earlier than originally planned. In Figure 7.8 there is an additional 15 minutes which cannot fit into period 2.

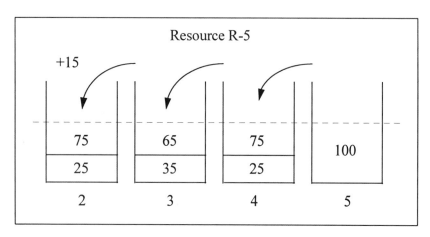

Figure 7.8   Dynamic buffering—an excess of 15 minutes remains.

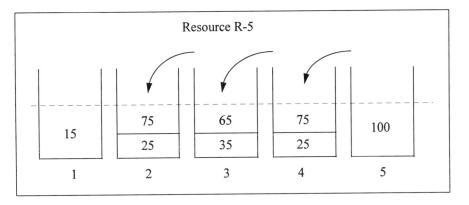

Figure 7.9 Dynamic buffering—excess 15 minutes is placed in period 1.

The fixed buffer is placed at the end of period 2, but additional time is required to ensure that resource R-5 can meet the demand of the constraint. So the additional demand is placed in period 1 (see Figure 7.9).

If the demand on the non-constraint is large enough, it will cause the release of raw material to occur earlier. Notice that 15 minutes of the demand was pushed into period 1. This means that the buffer for this portion of the net was enlarged by one period.

Dealing with prolonged periods at near-capacity levels

Whenever a resource has demand placed on it which exceeds the estimated protective capacity required to successfully meet the demands of the buffer origin, it may be necessary to introduce periods of artificial load which will take the place of real demand and force the buffer to be enlarged (see Figure 7.10).

Resource R-5 has been loaded to near-constraint levels for four consecutive periods. This means that, for those periods, whenever a problem arrives there is not enough protective capacity available on a temporary basis to deal with the problem. In Figure 7.11 an artificial load was placed on resource R-5 in period 2 which, in turn, increased the size of the buffer even though R-5 was never loaded over 100%.

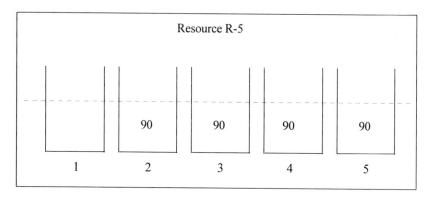

Figure 7.10   Dealing with prolonged demand at near-capacity levels.

Identifying the secondary constraint

The secondary constraint is that resource which has created the greatest threat to the protection provided by the system (the buffers). In the proceeding example, if resource R-5's demand were to be pushed so that it accumulated excess demand against time zero or excess load against an order which has already been scheduled on the constraint, then it is said to have created a peak load in period 1. While the largest peak load does not necessarily identify the secondary constraint, it is one among several clues which will help to identify the next problem resource.

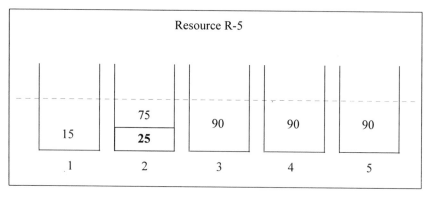

Figure 7.11   Applying artificial demand.

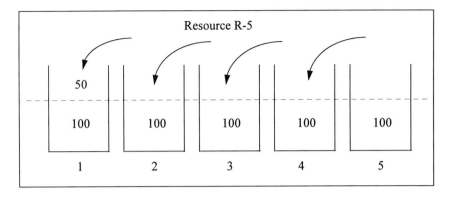

Figure 7.12 Peak load in period 1.

In Figure 7.12 the load is being steadily pushed from period 5 toward period 1. Since period 1 begins at time zero the load can no longer be pushed, and it begins to accumulate there. Notice that period 1 has 50% more load than it can handle.

When examined from a global perspective, the secondary constraint is that resource which has done the most damage to the protection needed for the system to perform to current demand. So to understand the impact of a peak load in the first period it must be compared in relationship to the protection (buffer) being used.

Resource R-1 in Figure 7.13 has an overload in period 1 of 50 %. Resource R-2 has an overload of 100%. The buffer sizes (protection) for both resources are exactly the same. This means that the relationship of the amount of overload to the amount of protection is much different for the two situations. Resource R-2 will have a more difficult time spreading the larger peak load among the various resources within the buffer than will resource R-1

In Figure 7.14 the size of the buffer has changed. Notice that the first period peak load for resource R-1 happens within a buffer whose size is 50% smaller. It has less opportunity to spread the load, which means that when setup savings or overtime are considered to solve the peak load problem, resource R-1 will have a greater problem in resolving the situation. It is therefore possible that R-1 may be the secondary constraint. A good measure for identifying the secondary constraint is the ratio between the buffer size and the overload.

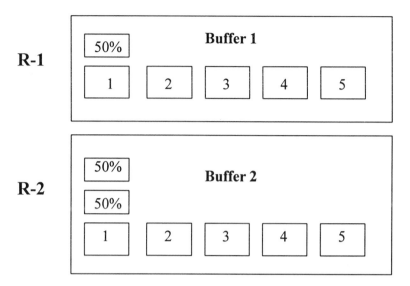

Figure 7.13   The relationship of the load to the size of the buffer.

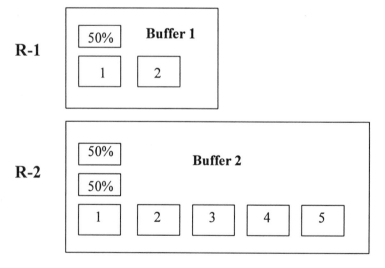

Figure 7.14   The relationship of the load to the size of the buffer—buffer 1 has been reduced.

If the amount of overload in minutes for period 1 exceeds the length of the buffer by a given amount, it is considered a problematic resource. That resource whose first period peak load exceeds the buffer size by a given amount greater than any other is identified as the secondary constraint.

Dealing with peak loads in the red lane

The *red lane* is defined as that area of the net which occurs between shipping and the primary constraint. It is particularly important because once the schedule has been set for the constraint and a large enough peak load is created on a resource existing in this area, it can threaten the schedule created by the constraint or result in pushing the sales order due date beyond its current schedule. The peak load problem for the red lane is handled the same way that a peak load is managed for those which occur at period 1. Whenever those resources are identified as being problematic (where the average demand exceeds the average capacity), the load is pushed toward time zero. However, in this case the load will be blocked from reaching time zero by an order or part/operation which has already been scheduled on the constraint. This order cannot be moved without damaging the constraint's schedule (see Figure 7.15).

Resource R-5 was scheduled passed 100% on days 24 and 25 and is pushing the load toward time zero. Part/operation A/20, which is fed by part/operation A/30 from the constraint schedule, was selected to be pushed into period 23. If pushed into an earlier period, would have been scheduled at day 23 hour 0:01. Notice that part/operation A/30 was scheduled to start on the constraint at day

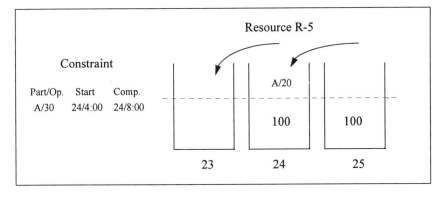

Figure 7.15 Peak loads in the red lane.

24 hour 4:00. Since A/30 feeds A/20 it would be impossible to have A/30 deliver to A/20 if A/20 is to start before A/30. A/20's demand must accumulate on day 25. Whenever the demand accumulates on a specific resource beyond a certain ratio in comparison with the buffer, it is declared a problematic resource. That resource which is declared problematic and accumulates more that any other resource in the red lane is a secondary constraint.

Creating Secondary Schedules

Schedules for secondary constraints derive their priority from the buffer origin they are trying to protect. They can be required to feed either the primary constraint, the shipping schedule, the assembly buffer, or another secondary constraint.

The initial phase of creating the secondary constraint is much the same as in the initial phase of the primary schedule. The first step is to place the orders on the time line in their ideal position based on the buffering system. The next step is to place the batches so that there are no conflicts with the existing schedule on the constraint.

Note: when interactive constraints exist only half the constraint buffer is used to set them apart (see Figure 7.16).

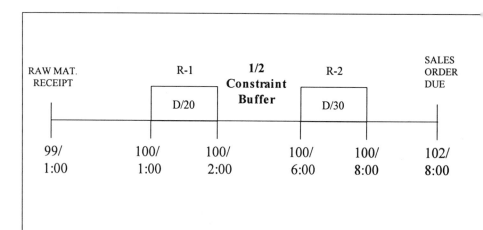

Figure 7.16   Interactive constraints.

Since D/20 feeds D/30 and D/20 is processed on the secondary constraint, then D/20's stop date and time will be one-half a constraint buffer width from the start time of D/30 on the primary constraint. If the constraint buffer was normally 8 hours and D/30 starts at day 100 hour 6:00, then D/20 should stop at day 100 hour 2:00.

Notice that D/20's buffer is a full constraint width. The gating operation is scheduled to release raw material at day 99 hour 1:00. Notice also that the protection in front of the primary constraint is now 50% larger because a secondary constraint was declared. Material is released 50% earlier. Whenever a secondary constraint is declared in front of the primary constraint in the system inventory will go up.

Resolving conflicts between schedules

The secondary constraint's schedule may look much the same as the primary schedule did as orders were initially placed on the time line. However, with the secondary constraint there may be conflicts which arise when trying to place the load. It is advantageous for every order to be placed with enough time to ensure that the material will reach the buffer origin in time. As part/operations are moved in the process of exploitation, some orders will inevitably be placed closer to the schedule on the constraint than is desired

Resolving conflict between schedules means ensuring that part/operations are protected in time. Like the rods discussed in Chapter 6 used to keep part/operations apart as they cross the constraint, rods are also used between schedules of two different constraining resources. Rod timing is computed exactly as in Chapter 6.

Figure 7.17 is an example of a forward rod used on multiple constraints. Resource R-4 is the primary constraint and is fed by resource R-3. R-3 is the secondary constraint and is connected by forward rods 1 and 2, which originate from part/operation A and connect to part/operation B. During the scheduling process, the rods prevent part/operation A from approaching part operation B by less than one-half the constraint buffer. Notice that these rods are connected between two different schedules. Since part/operation B was scheduled first on the primary constraint it does not move. A must be scheduled around B. (Time runs from left to right.) The objective here is to ensure that after part/operation A is processed on the secondary constraint it will have enough time to travel to the primary constraint. R-4 is still the constraint and part/operation A still feeds part/operation B. However, A is now being processed on the primary

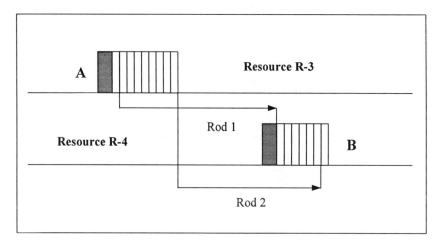

Figure 7.17   Forward rods on multiple constraints.

constraint. As R-3's orders are being placed on the time line, rods 1 and 2 prevent B from approaching A by less that 1/2 the constraint buffer.

Figure 7.18 is an example of backward rods on multiple constraints.

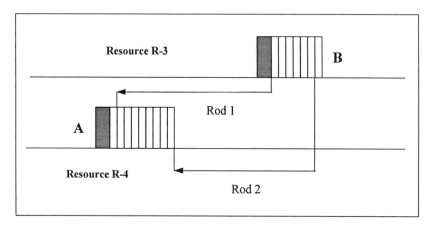

Figure 7.18   Backward rods on multiple constraints.

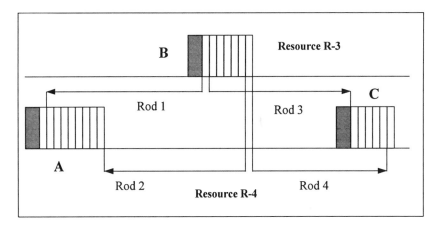

Figure 7.19 Combination rods on multiple constraints.

Figure 7.19 is an example of combination rods between two resources. Resource R-4 is still the constraint. A and C are part/operations which have established schedules on the primary constraint. B must try to fit between A and C without disturbing their schedules. B must therefore be scheduled so that it does not violate rods in both directions. Because it must be placed between two established batches on the primary constraint, this is the most difficult batch to place in time and is given priority during the subordination phase.

Note: it is possible to have primary and secondary constraints which do not interact in any way. In this case rods are not required. Each part/operation resource is scheduled independently of one another.

Placing the load

The placement of the load for the initial schedule is according to the ideal location without consideration for the load or conflicts which may exist.

The first orders to be placed on the schedule for the secondary constraint are those that have combination rods. Part/operation 1 on the constraint feeds part/operation 6 with an intermediate operation on resource R-1. R-1 is the secondary constraint. Part/operation D in R-1's schedule must be placed in time between 1 and 6 and be separated by combination rods equal to one-half the constraint buffer. D is placed according to the backward time rod (see Figure 7.20).

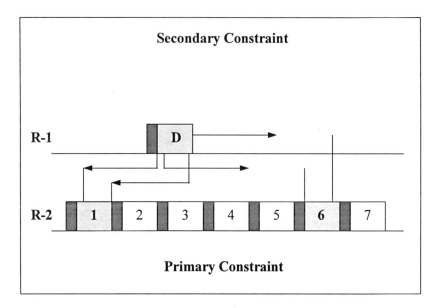

Figure 7.20 Placing the load according to the rods.

The next orders to be placed are those with forward time rods. The placement is one-half buffer constraint distance behind the connecting order on the constraint (see Figure 7.21). Part/operation B from resource R-1 feeds part/operation 4 on the constraint and has been placed one-half buffer length prior to part/operation 4. Part/operation E was placed one-half buffer length in front of 7.

Notice that part/operations B and D are trying to occupy the same position on the schedule for R-1. When the final schedule is created, D will have priority in placement over B since D has combination rods and was placed first. Notice also that B has room to move to the left and not violate the forward time rods to 4.

The next placement is for orders with backward time rods. They are placed one-half constraint buffer distance in front of the connecting order on the constraint (see Figure 7.22). Order F on resource R-1 is being fed by order 3 on resource R-2 and was placed one-half constraint buffer width behind order 3. Order G is connected to order 5.

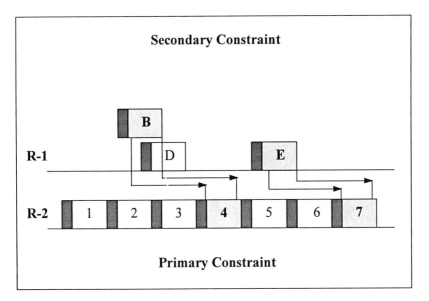

Figure 7.21 Placing the load according to the rods.

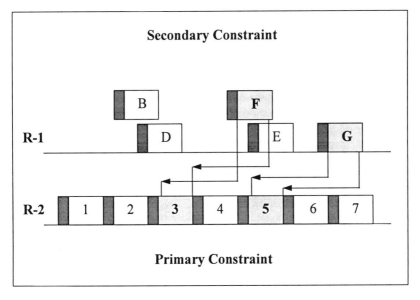

Figure 7.22 Placing the load according to the rods.

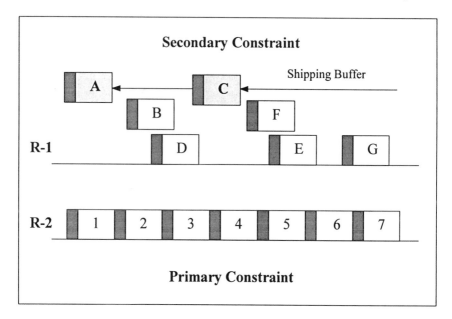

Figure 7.23 Placing the load according to the buffer.

Notice that E and F are also trying to occupy the same space on the schedule for R-1. In this case priority will go to E since it has already been placed. Due to the backward rods to 3, F can only move forward in time to be placed.

Orders with connecting orders on the secondary constraint are placed one-half buffer distance behind the order which it feeds (see Figure 7.23). A feeds C on the same schedule so it is placed one-half buffer width in front of C. C is scheduled based on the shipping buffer.

Finally, the initial placement of orders which do not have connecting orders on any constraint are placed one shipping buffer from the due date of the sales order.

EXPLOITING THE SECONDARY CONSTRAINT

To exploit the secondary constraint means to schedule it so that there are no conflicts with the primary constraint and also so that the amount of available

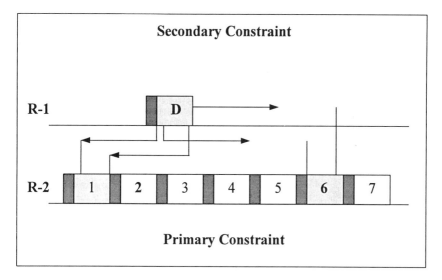

Figure 7.24 Scheduling the secondary constraint.

time is optimized to protect the constraint or any other buffer origin that the secondary constraint is feeding.

The first step in the process is to place the orders on the time line based on the various buffer types. This was accomplished in the last section. The next phase is to level the load on the secondary constraint (R-1). Orders must be placed so that there are no conflicts with the constraint's schedule, the schedule for the secondary constraint, time zero or the shipping buffer.

The first order to be placed during the initial placement on the time line was D (see Figure 7.24). During the leveling process, D's position is not going to change. The next orders to be placed are those with forward rods (see Figure 7.25). Notice that the conflict between B and D has been solved. Since B could move to a position earlier in time it did not violate its forward time rods to 4 and no longer occupies the same place with D. Notice that E's position was not affected.

The next orders to be placed are those with backward rods (see Figure 7.26). F and G are pushed forward in time and placed immediately after F. Notice the additional distance between F and G and their corresponding orders on R-2

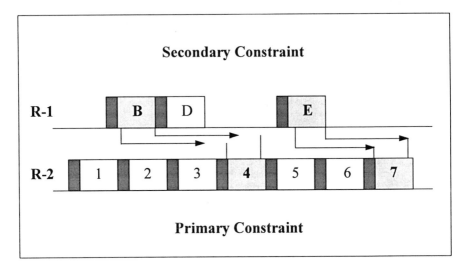

Figure 7.25   Scheduling the secondary constraint—placing orders with forward rods.

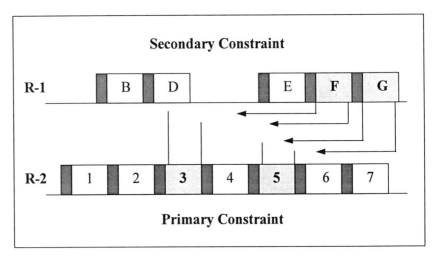

Figure 7.26   Scheduling the secondary constraint—placing orders with backward rods.

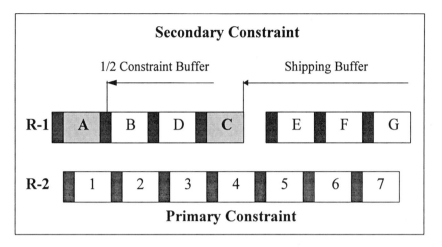

Figure 7.27 Scheduling the secondary constraint.

The last orders to be placed on R-1 are those which do not have any connection to R-2 (see Figure 7.27). A feeds B on resource R-1 and is scheduled one-half buffer width in front of C. The arrows for the shipping and one-half constraint buffer have been placed in relative position. Notice that A has been moved to the left a short distance and placed in front of B. Notice also that C was moved a short distance toward the right and into the shipping buffer. Fortunately the schedule did not require more than a small portion of the protection of C to resolve all conflicts between the schedules for R-1 and R-2. Had C been pushed farther to the right so that it took more than half the shipping buffer, the sales order which C feeds would be considered late and pushed into the future. Notice that there is a gap between orders C and E. In order to solve the conflict between the schedules, no orders are allowed to occupy this space.

The objective in exploiting R-1 is not to maximize its production. Once all conflicts have been resolved, the scheduling process stops. Had there not been enough capacity on R-1 to resolve all the conflicts and handle the load, issues such as setup savings would be considered. In this case it was not needed.

The Timing and Direction of Order Processing

In placing the load and scheduling R-1 there was a certain priority in the sequence that the orders were placed. One issue not discussed was the direction in which processing takes place:

- When placing the orders with combination rods, since each order is placed at the end of the backward rod, the process begins with the earliest order and moves to the latest.
- When placing orders with forward rods the timing of placement moves from the latest orders to the earliest.

Once the orders with combination and forward rods have been placed, an adjustment should be made for time zero. All the orders which have been placed past time zero should be pushed into the present. The resulting schedule should reveal any conflicts which exist in the two schedules. If no conflict exists:

- The orders with backward rods are placed moving from earliest to latest.

If there is still no conflict:

- Those orders with no rods are placed from the latest to the earliest.

Note: if a conflict arises between the primary and secondary constraint which cannot be resolved during the scheduling process, orders on the constraint are pushed into a later time period, resulting in sales orders being scheduled further out in time. Once this occurs, the scheduling process of the primary constraint must begin again with the new schedule date for the sales orders as input.

PROCESSING ON THE NET

Unlike material requirements planning, which uses a concept called low level coding to determine the order of processing, the TOC based system uses time. In low level coding MRP waits until that level in the product structure has been reached where all of the parent requirements and timing for a specific part have been computed before processing the gross to net requirements (see Figure 7.28).

Part C appears on three different levels in the product structure. Before gross to net requirement generation is performed all of the planned releases for the parent items for C must have already been computed down to and including level 4.

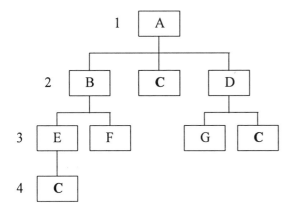

Figure 7.28 Low level coding.

In the TOC system, time is used. Since the system works with time as the controlling factor, knowing when something is to occur is the key issue. There are two places in time that are known to the system when the subordination process starts. One is the time when the sales orders are due, and the other is the schedule for the primary constraint. Thus, when moving in time these two issues must be considered.

The system starts with a block of time at the end of the schedule and determines what activity must take place during that time block. The next time block to be considered is the one which exists toward time zero from the end of the horizon. All activity for the first time period must be concluded before moving to the next.

Activity for a certain time block may be nothing more than computing when to place a specific order's part/operation in time so that when the system reaches that date while moving toward time zero it can place the load on the associated resource.

The system starts with a known occurrence at the end of the planning horizon. This will be a sales order. A list is used to keep track of those items which are identified in the current time as needing some sort of activity but for which action is to take place at a later time.

In Figure 7.29 the system starts with the end of the planning horizon and moves in time constantly toward the present. Actions which are to be performed within certain time periods are done as the specific timing of that action reaches what is considered by the system as current time. Current time is the specific block of time that the system is working in as it moves from the end of the planning horizon to the present. As an example, when the system is computing requirements for day 200, then day 200 is the current day.

Before moving toward day 199, the system must complete all of the tasks that are assigned to be completed in day 200. Notice that in day 200 there is a sales orders for a quantity of 20 As.

One of the issues facing the system on day 200 is what must be done with the part/operations which feed shipping for sales order S/O111. Notice that Part/operations A/30, A/20 and A/10 appear on a list of things to do on day 198. In this case the shipping buffer is 2 days long and, based on the requirements of the sales order, the system made a decision to place these part/operations on a list for day 198.

Figure 7.30 is the net that this data came from. The question which should be raised at this time is why stop at A/10? Why weren't part/operations B/30 or D/30 placed in day 198?

The objective in processing on the net is to find those things which have no place in time and to give them one relative to their position within the net. B/30 for sales order S/O111 is processed on the primary constraint. It already has its place in time. D/30 must be scheduled based on the assembly buffer established at A/10, so it would occupy a different day. If the assembly buffer

Figure 7.29   Moving in time.

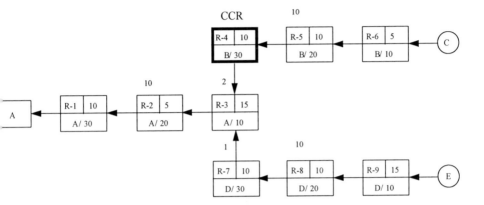

Figure 7.30 Processing on the net.

for A/10 were one day, then D/30, D/20 and D/10 would occupy day 197 (see Figure 7.31).

Once the processing down the net reaches a raw material part, the processing stops. The system returns to the highest assembly operation and processes down the other leg placing part/operations on the list of things to do when the system's current date and the date of the list match.

Notice that after processing down the bottom leg in Figure 7.30 when an attempt is made to process down the top leg, the first part/operation after the

197	198	199	200
D/30 D/20 D/10	A/30 A/20 A/10		S/O111 A Qty - 20

Figure 7.31 Moving in time.

assembly is the constraint. Since the constraint has its place in time already, the processing stops and the next sales order is processed.

All sales orders for period 200 have been processed, so the current day moves to day 199. No orders exist in day 199 so the system again shifts the current day and it becomes day 198. Day 198 contains three part/operations originally placed by sales order S/O111, and each is to be processed on different resources. At this time the required setup and run times for each part/operation are placed on their respective resources. If an overload is detected by the system, the excess time will be pushed into an earlier time period as in Figure 7.9.

If additional sales orders existed in period 198, they would have been processed also. However, since there were none the processing for day 198 is complete and the current day shifts again to day 197. On day 197 three part/operations are to be placed on their respective resources.

The next question that might be asked is why wasn't the inventory at operation A/20 considered when placing A/20 and A/30 in day 198. Remember that the process starts at the end of the horizon, not the beginning. That inventory has already been allocated to another order earlier in time. The first pass in processing on the net is to start from the present and move toward the end of the planning horizon allocating inventory.

The next step would be to place B/20 and B/10. When the system date reaches the date that B/30 crosses R-4 on the constraint schedule, B/20 and B/30 will be placed one constraint buffer in time in front of B/30 for sales order S/O111.

SETTING THE SCHEDULE FOR DIVERGING OPERATIONS

The last subject to be discussed is the scheduling of diverging operations. Whenever one operation feeds two operations, the opportunity for the misallocation of material is very real. Material which is allocated to one part/operation on a specific resource may be taken by another. The usual reason is to promote the maximal utilization of one resource over another (see Figure 7.32).

Resource R-5 has 15 parts which have been completed at part/operation G/30. The questions which must be answered are how many parts go to resource R-2 for processing E/10 and how many go to R-4 for processing F/10. If R-2 were

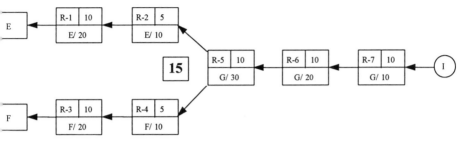

Figure 7.32   Diverging operations.

processing another part when time became available on R-4, R-4 would need to begin processing the G/30 parts. But how many should R-4 process? If R-4 were to stop at 5 parts and R-2 were still busy, there would be a tendency for R-4 to continue processing until all the G/30s were gone. Some of the G/30s would be needed to process the sales demand for E. However, there are no more G/30s left at resource R-5. They have all gone to be processed on those resources which feed F. To solve this problem a schedule must be created for R-2 and R-4. The key issue being how many parts to process and when.

While processing on the net, special treatment is given to those resources which process material arriving from diverging operations. A schedule is created consisting of a simple list of what parts must be processed that are arriving from diverging part/operations and which resource gets what quantity and when. Of the 15 parts in Figure 7.32, 5 may be scheduled for order E and 10 may be scheduled for order F.

SUMMARY

The subordination process is important in that it defines how the remaining resources are subordinated to the demands of the schedule created for the primary constraint. The key issues are

- Providing the constraint what it needs to perform to the schedule created during the subordination phase
- Exploiting of secondary constraints
- Overcoming conflicts which may exist between the primary and any secondary constraints
- Processing on the net
- Buffering the remaining system

Subordination is an integral part of the five-step process of improvement and as such must be included in the construction of the information system.

STUDY QUESTIONS

1. Define dynamic buffering and explain its overall importance to the scheduling process

2. Explain the difference between the fixed and variable portions of the buffer.

3. What is the rule of thumb when establishing the initial buffer length to use when implementing a manual DBR process?

4. What is dynamic buffering and what is its impact on subordination?

5. What problems could be encountered between the primary and secondary constraint in creating a valid schedule?

6. Explain the sequence and direction of movement when placing orders on the time line with specific rod types.

7. Explain the process of moving in time on the net

8. Define the concepts of diverging and converging operations, explain at what time each may need a schedule, and provide insight into the kinds of problems which are caused by the overutilization of resources when confronted with these two characteristics.

9. Define the term *resource activation.*

10. What provisions have been made for dealing with prolonged periods at near-capacity levels on non-constrained resources.

11. What is meant by the concept of a peak load on day 1, or in the red lane, and how does the system deal with these problems?

8

Buffer Management

The buffer is used to set the amount of protection needed by the system during the scheduling process and to set the raw materials schedule. However, it is not enough just to set the schedule. It must be controlled so that those things which are supposed to happen, do. Buffer management represents the control portion of the system. It is used to ensure that if something goes wrong, it can be detected and fixed before there is an impact which will threaten the creation of throughput. There are two issues:

- To identify those orders which are having problems and rectify the situation so that the orders will not be late
- To identify and fix those things which consistently make orders late

CHAPTER OBJECTIVES

- To present the buffer management concept
- To understand the relationship between buffer management and the improvement process
- To present methods of using the system to accomplish buffer management

Buffer management is an important part of the TOC based system. As seen in Figure 8.1, it plays a part in identifying and exploiting the constraint as well as establishing the subordination process. Used effectively buffer management:

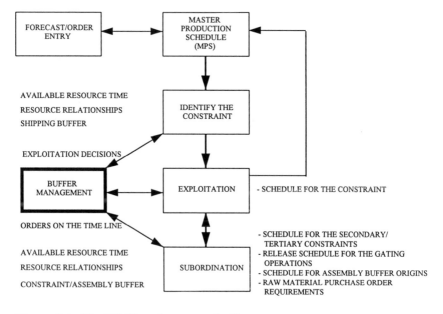

Figure 8.1 The TOC based system—buffer management.

- Helps to identify and correct those orders which are having problems in reaching the buffer origin before they can affect the generation of throughput
- Establishes the focal mechanism for ensuring that when an action is taken to improve the amount of protection available in the system that there will be an immediate impact on the reduction of inventory and operating expense
- Prioritizes problems in order of relative importance so that those issues having the greatest impact can be addressed first
- Aids in establishing the length of the fixed portion of the buffer

IDENTIFYING PROBLEM ORDERS

One of the objectives in buffer management is to identify problem orders before they impact the buffer origin. Problem orders are those orders which will threaten the creation of throughput. If they can be detected and action is taken early enough, then the buffer origin is adequately protected.

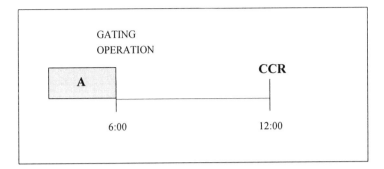

Figure 8.2 Identifying problem orders.

In Figure 8.2, order A must travel from the gating operation, beginning at 6:00, through all the intermediate operations and arrive at the capacity constrained resource (CCR) by 12:00. To arrive later than 12:00 means to lose throughput by not having an order to process on the CCR. However, it does not help to look at the order at 12:00 and determine that it has not arrived; a loss in throughput will probably be unavoidable. To effectively protect the constraint, the time to examine A is before it is scheduled to arrive.

In Figure 8.3 the time in front of the constraint on which A is to be processed has been divided into three different zones. Notice that zone I is from 10:00 until 12:00 and is called the expedite zone. If A does not arrive at the constraint before 10:00 it is located and expedited so that it will reach the constraint at least by 12:00, when it is to be processed. Zone II is from 8:00 until 10:00 and is called the tracking zone. If A does not arrive at the constraint before 8:00 it is located and tracked to see if problems might be developing. Zone III is considered normal time and runs from 6:00 when the order is released until 8:00 when the tracking zone begins.

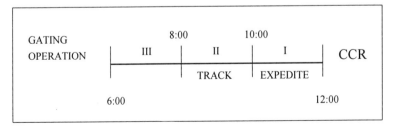

Figure 8.3 The buffer zones.

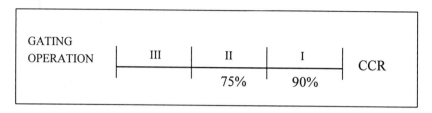

Figure 8.4 The zone cross section.

The Zone Profile

Not only is it possible to identify those orders that are getting into trouble and expediting them, but also it is possible to look at a cross section of how well the system is performing based on the percentage of those orders that either do or do not arrive at the constraint within a particular zone. In Figure 8.4, 90% of all orders are sitting in front of the constraint within zone I. 75% are arriving within zone II. This cross section means that for the CCR in Figure 8.4, 10% of the orders are being expedited.

A lower percentage of on-time arrivals could mean that the buffer is too small. The cross section in Figure 8.5 means that 25% of all orders are being expedited. If parts are being released too late, then the orders would arrive late. In order to solve this problem either the buffer should be lengthened or the cause of the late orders discovered and fixed.

Figure 8.6 represents the zone profile of a buffer origin as it appears at 1:00. A number of orders are approaching the buffer origin. Each order has its own place in time. Order number 1 starts at 1:00 and runs until approximately 1:25. Order 2 starts at 1:25 and runs until 1:45. The shaded areas with bold numbers indicate that the order has arrived at the buffer origin. At 1:00 zone I has all of its orders, zone II is short one order and zone III has none.

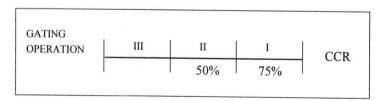

Figure 8.5 The zone cross section—buffer too small.

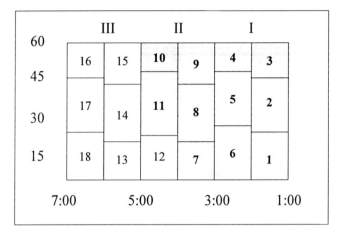

Figure 8.6 Buffer management—zone profile of buffer origin at 1:00.

Different zone profiles point to the occurrence of specific problems. Figure 8.7 shows another buffer. Notice that at 1:00 all orders except number 18 have arrived for all the zones. This is a good indication that the fixed portion of the buffer is too long and should be shortened. Figure 8.8 indicates that the buffer may be too short. Only half of zone I is filled. The numbers on the left represent time in 15 minute intervals. If this picture of the buffer is correct, then the buffer manager has 1 hour to find more work for the constraint or it will be idle.

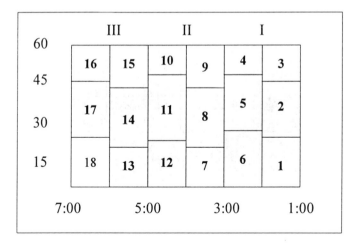

Figure 8.7 Zone profile at 1:00 showing buffer too long.

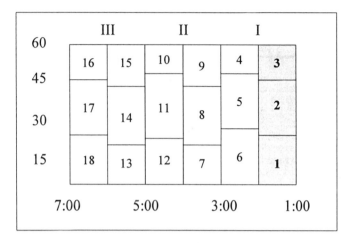

Figure 8.8 Zone profile at 1:00 showing buffer too short.

The situation in Figure 8.9 is much better than in Figure 8.8. However, notice that two orders are missing from zone I, while other orders have arrived at zone II. Since there are other orders available in front of the constraint, this situation is not as bad. There is approximately 3 hours 10 minutes of work available. However, it does indicate that something must be wrong with the orders which

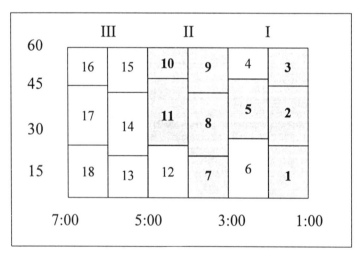

Figure 8.9 Zone profile at 1:00 showing holes in the buffer.

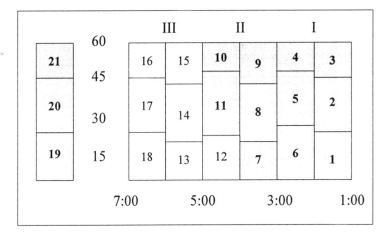

Figure 8.10 Zone profile at 1:00 showing orders released too early.

were supposed to appear in positions 4 and 6. They should be found and expedited, and the cause listed on the buffer management worksheet.

Figure 8.10 shows orders which have arrived at the constraint, but are not inside any of the buffer management zones. Orders which arrive too early are an indication that they were released before their scheduled release date. This is usually caused by workers or supervisors who have a problem understanding that sometimes resources are idle for a reason. However, because the sequencing of work at non-constraint operations is determined by the release schedule at gating operations, having an order arrive early at the constraint may mean that a temporary bottleneck will be created. The early order might have taken a specific resource time slot that was meant for another order.

THE BUFFER MANAGEMENT WORKSHEET

Whenever the cause of an order's lateness in arriving at zone I is detected, it is placed on the buffer management worksheet maintained by the buffer manager. The list is consolidated and used to prioritize the order in which problems are fixed. Figure 8.11 is taken from *The Next Phase of Total Quality Management* (1994) and represents a buffer management worksheet.

This kind of worksheet can easily be placed into the shop floor control portion of any system for collecting data concerning the health of the system. As

			ZONE I	ZONE I
LOC	STATION	CAUSE	DUE	ACT.
R-1	A/30	MATERIAL SHORT	101/3:15	101/5:15
R-1	A/20	BROKEN FIXTURE	101/5:30	101/5:45
R-2	A/30	OUT OF SPEC.	101/5:45	101/7:17

BUFFER ORIGIN: RESOURCE R-4   DATE: 09/02/95

BUFFER LENGTH: 16 HRS   ZONE DISTRIBUTION: I   90%   II   75%

Figure 8.11 The buffer management worksheet.

material arrives at the buffer origin, it is logged and an automatic percentage rating for each zone of the buffer can be calculated.

A buffer management report can be generated from the input data similar to Figure 8.12, also taken from *The Next Phase of Total Quality Management.* Notice that the throughput dollar days have been calculated for each cause so the effort to fix problems that cause holes in the buffer can be placed in proper perspective. Throughput dollar days (T$Ds) are calculated as the length of time

BUFFER ORIGIN: RESOURCE B   DATE: 02/27/94

BUFFER LENGTH: 16 HRS   ZONE DISTRIBUTION: I   90%   II   75%

			TOTAL		T	
LOC	STATION	CAUSE	TIME		VALUE	T$D
R-1	123/30	REWORK FOR SIZE	.5	×	$1,000	$500
R-1	123/20	KEYWAY TOO SMALL	1.0	×	$2,000	$2,000
R-2	121/30	MATERIAL SHORT	2.0	×	$1,500	$3,000

Figure 8.12 The buffer management report.

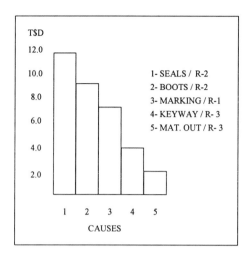

Figure 8.13 Pareto analysis to determine priority of buffer problems.

that the order was late getting to the constraint in zone I times the amount of throughput that was threatened. At resource R-1 part/operation 123/30 was reworked for size, causing the order to be 1/2 day late. Multiplied by the $1,000 of throughput generated by the order, the total throughput dollar days for the offense is $500. Compared to R-1's problem, R-2's, which caused $3,000 in throughput dollar days to accumulate, was a greater threat to the creation of throughput.

After collecting the data, a Pareto analysis is performed to determine the priority of effort spent to solve the problems (see Figure 8.13). The number one priority seems to be the seals problem at resource R-2 which has accumulated 12,000 dollars in throughput dollar days. Number two is the boot problem. So the premier effort to increase the protection in front of the buffer origin should be to fix the problems with the seals, and the next to fix the boots problem.

Accumulating Throughput Dollar Days by Department

In addition to focusing efforts to ensure that the primary causes of orders being late are fixed, attention must also be given to making sure that orders are expedited effectively. Any order which becomes late will begin collecting throughput dollar days for the department where the order is currently located. The later it becomes or the higher the dollar value, the greater the pressure becomes to move the order to the next department. As soon as the late order leaves the department, the accumulated T$Ds immediately drop for that department but increase for the succeeding department. This will continue until the order is shipped.

Inventory Dollar Days

There are certain actions which will have a negative effect on the system because they happen too early. As an example, if material is released to the gating operation earlier than the scheduled release date, inventory will increase. If material is processed too early at another operation the result may be that parts in the production process will be mismatched. After the schedule has been created and instructions are given for the timing of specific events, the inventory dollar day (I$D) measurement is used to provide an incentive for preventing an activity from occurring too soon. It establishes the relative value of a specific activity. Here, the value of the inventory increased by the action is multiplied by the number of days that are affected. As the value in the measurement increases, the pressure will increase to prevent the activity from occurring. As for throughput dollar days, a Pareto analysis of the inventory dollar days assigned to a specific cause or department will lead to an understanding of where to focus activity to improve.

THE BUFFER MANAGER

Companies having implemented TOC in a manufacturing environment have found a need for a person to ensure that the buffer is maintained. This is a very important position. If the buffer is too long, this person is responsible to shorten it in the system, and vice versa. If there are holes in zone I of the buffer, orders must be expedited and data collected.

SUMMARY

Buffer management can offer a unique and powerful tool to increase the effectiveness of the scheduling system by controlling events and preventing them from negatively affecting the buffer origin. It is easily reproduced in the information system once the schedule has been created and will readily fit into shop floor control.

Used effectively the buffer management system can also help tremendously in the focusing process by identifying those actions which need to be fixed in the

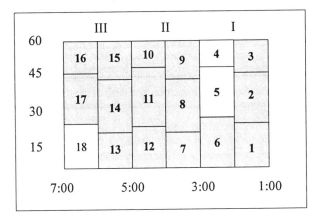

60

III   II   I

| 16 | 15 | 10 | 9 | 4 | 3 |

45

| 17 | | 11 | | 5 | 2 |
| | 14 | | 8 | | |

30

15

| 18 | 13 | 12 | 7 | 6 | 1 |

7:00   5:00   3:00   1:00

Figure 8.14 Buffer management example for study question 6.

schedule to increase the amount of protection available for the buffer origin and to reduce inventory and operating expense.

STUDY QUESTIONS

1. Define the concept of buffer management and describe the primary responsibilities of the buffer manager.

2. Explain what is meant by the *tracking* and *expedite zones*.

3. What is a zone profile and what is its primary function?

4. What are the purposes of the buffer management worksheet and the buffer management report?

5. Define and give examples of the use of the measurements *throughput dollar days* and *inventory dollar days*.

6. What situation(s) is indicated by the graphical representation of the buffer shown in Figure 8.14?

9

Supporting the Decision Process

Once a complete definition of an information system has been made, how then should it be used? The system can provide information that will aid in the process of answering specific day-to-day questions such as what lot size should be used and what price should be accepted for this product.

CHAPTER OBJECTIVES

- To introduce the decision support features of the system
- To relate how the information system should be used to make decisions

The information system was designed to provide valid information, not just schedule and control the factory. While a valid schedule and an effective control mechanism are prerequisites to the information system and are a tremendous breakthrough: it is the assistance in strategic as well as day-to-day decision-making which maximizes the system's effectiveness in helping the user to generate a profit.

Note: a detailed discussion of the fundamentals of the decision-making process can be found in *The Next Phase of Total Quality Management* (1994). This portion of the book will be dedicated to using the information system to accomplish this task.

Before continuing, it must be understood that the information system, like any other computer system, is merely a tool. Used incorrectly, the desired result will never come to fruition. Used correctly by intelligent and knowledgeable people, the information system can serve as a valid replacement for the current manufacturing schedule and control system as well as cost accounting. However, it will never run the company nor should it be considered infallible. Management's intuition about a particular issue in running the company is sometimes more accurate.

MAKING DECISIONS

Keep in mind that information is defined here as the answer to the question asked. How each department within the organization should use the system must be determined in the context of the decisions made. It is the individual tasks to be performed which define the requirements. Since the objective is to implement the five-step process of improvement, the action required depends on where in the process the decision is being made.

The discussion of how to use the system to make decisions will be placed in the context of the two major categories of *tactical* and *strategic* decisions.

- Tactical decisions—those decisions made on a day-to-day basis to run the company
- Strategic decisions—those decisions that plot the direction of the company's future for years to come

Tactical decisions include issues such as

- Where to focus improvements in the factory
- Whether to accept a specific offer for a sales order
- Whether a particular part should be purchased outside the company or made internally

These are the kinds of decisions that keep the wheels turning on a daily basis. Strategic decisions include issues such as

- Market segmentation
- Company growth
- Long-term planning
- Recession proofing the company

Strategic decisions are extremely important. A mistake here usually results in long-term problems and even bankruptcy.

Note: strategic decisions will be discussed in Chapter 10.

Tactical Decisions

A complete discussion of how the information system should support the decision process could not anticipate every decision that is to be made. The objective here is not to present every possible situation but to convey to the reader the basic issues involved with using the system to make the day-to-day decisions normally faced in the manufacturing environment. Tactical decisions will be discussed on a departmental basis, as follows:

- Purchasing
- Finance and accounting
- Quality
- Engineering
- Sales and marketing
- Production

PURCHASING

The general purchasing questions that must be answered are what to order, when to schedule delivery and what to pay for raw material items. The TOC based manufacturing system creates a list of raw material purchasing requirements similar to material requirements planning. In fact, the material requirements messaging facility for most MRP based systems works very well in controlling the purchase of raw material for production. What the TOC based system provides that MRP cannot is a valid schedule of requirements that closely resembles the way in which the material is consumed. Additionally, it provides feedback to the purchasing agent or manager regarding the impact or importance of a specific order.

Scheduling has proven to be very capable at handling the what and when questions. But how should the system regard the issues involving the cost of raw material? Since the goal of purchasing must be to protect the creation of throughput, the discussion should probably begin there.

Purchasing conflicts generally deal with the protection or the creation of throughput; common scenarios are

- The cost of a part is perceived to be too high in comparison to the individual profit margin obtained for the product.

- The vendor's perception of the value of the product is in conflict with the purchaser's.

So it seems that one advantage the information system could provide the purchasing department is to ensure that the purchasing agent understands the true value of the part being bought. This was the original intent of cost accounting. As discussed earlier, however, cost accounting long ago ceased providing a benefit.

The true value of a part is determined by the benefit derived. This brings up an interesting question. How can the purchasing agent sitting in an office perhaps hundreds of miles from the factory understand what benefit a specific part will have? Can the system help?

There are some key issues involved in understanding this problem. Besides the obvious raw material expense, there is a difference in the value of a part, which depends on whether it is

- Processed on the constraint
- Using protective capacity
- Using excess capacity

Parts Processed on the Constraint

Sometimes it is better to determine the value of a part by looking at its absence. For instance, what is the value of not having a part which feeds the constraint? Is it different than for a non-constraint? How will that impact the perception of the worth of the product to the purchasing agent? (See Figure 9.1.)

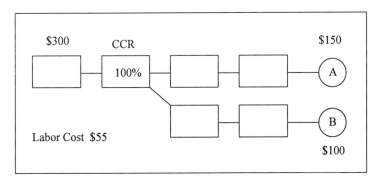

Figure 9.1 Purchasing decision example.

Raw material A and B feed resources which eventually feed the constraint. In order to complete a sales order valued at $300, both A and B are needed. The normal price for A is $75; the standard cost is in the computer at $80. The vendor has some As located in another city and can have them air-freighted at double the price. B's cost is set at $100 and is available. Labor cost is an additional $55. The normal gross margin on this product is 23%. However, in this case the company is looking at a total cost of goods sold (COGS) of $305. From a cost accounting perspective spending the additional money to obtain the part is a losing proposition. The question is how can the system help solve this problem for the purchasing agent.

The first thing that can be eliminated from the equation is the $55 labor cost. Most companies pay based on a 40 hour week regardless of where the labor goes. That leaves the issue of whether the part should be flown in or delayed for a better price. If the part is not obtained and the constraint runs out of work, there will be an immediate $300 loss in total revenue being received by the company. There is a limited amount of capacity on the constraint that, once lost, can never be regained. If the part is obtained and the capacity constrained resource is able to continue working, the company makes $50 ($300 − $250) and keeps the customer happy.

What did the purchasing agent need to be able to make the decision?

- Information that part A fed the constraint
- Information on whether there is a hole in the buffer that cannot be recovered by processing another order
- The sales price of the end item
- The cost of raw material

If this is the information needed to make the decision, then obviously this is what the system must provide. If the constraint were unknown, the purchasing agent would first need to identify it. Clearly, the TOC based manufacturing system is capable of accomplishing this task. However, in any company which has implemented TOC and has a physical constraint in production it is not kept a deep dark secret. Quite the opposite is true. So what purchasing needs is a method of identifying

- Orders which cause holes in the buffer
- The raw material parts required
- The sales price of the products that will be impacted

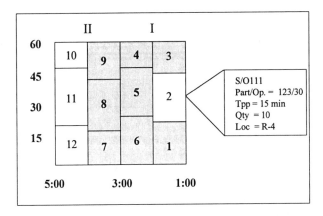

Figure 9.2 Buffer management example.

- The current cost of all raw material for the product/line item involved
- The projected due date of the purchase order line item in question

In Figure 9.2, part/operation 123/30 of order number 2 in zone I of the buffer has not arrived at the constraint. This order is late because raw material part A has not yet been delivered by the vendor. This is not an acceptable situation. While additional orders are in zone I and can be used to fill the position of order 2, the probability is quite good that something else will occur that will threaten the constraint even further.

It's obvious that raw material A must be received very quickly. However, if the value of the sales order is $300, it makes no sense to pay $10,000 to get the part. So what should purchasing be willing to pay?

Figure 9.3 is a raw material pegging report screen for all raw material parts which feed the constraint. Included in the data are

- Raw material part
- Quantity of the raw material required
- Part/operation which is to be processed on the constraint
- Product involved
- Sales order
- Sales order value
- Total raw material cost included in the product

		Raw Material Pegging/Constraint					
Raw Mat.	Qty Req.	CCR Part/Op	Product	Sales Ord.	S/O Value	Total RM Cost
A	10	123/30	F	S/O111	$300	$100
A	20	124/20	G	S/O222	$150	$50
B	15	125/20	G	S/O222		
C.	10	127/30	H.	S/O333	$200	$100

Figure 9.3 Raw material pegging report.

Notice that a quantity of 10 As are required to feed part/operation 123/30. Notice also that sales order S/O111 is valued at $300 and has a total raw material content of $100.

This means that purchasing can pay up to an additional $199 for the 10 part As that will be used on part/operation 123/30 to fill sales order S/O111 and the company will still show a $1 profit. If there are not enough orders in the buffer to insure that the constraint continues to generate throughput and the raw material does not arrive in time, then the constraint will be idle and the company will lose $300.

Note: whenever a sales order is threatened, the urgency of the customer's needs must also play a part. Sales must become involved. Ultimately it is a management decision.

Off-Loading Constraint Time to the Vendor During Scheduling

If all the demand for the constraint's time can be filled through exploitation without making orders late, then all parts should be produced in-house. However, if during the scheduling process all attempts to generate a schedule for the constraint fail to eliminate late orders, they can either be pushed into the future or additional resource time can be purchased. Purchasing additional constraint time includes off-loading constraint time to a vendor.

Note: off-loading to a vendor is similar to the issues involved with off-loading to an internal resource. The earlier in the process that off-loading takes place, the more orders will be impacted.

			A		
Total Sales	$30,000		300		
Total RM	$20,000		250		
Throughput	$10,000	+	50	=	10,050

Figure 9.4 Off-loading to a vendor example calculation.

In making the decision, the amount of additional expense for purchasing resource time to process the part is added to the total cost of raw material for the product to determine the amount of throughput generated. If purchasing resource time will still generate a positive throughput figure, then the impact will be to increase total throughput (see Figure 9.4).

The total sales of the company based on the schedule is $30,000 per week, while the total raw material required is $20,000. Product A has been sold for $300. The total cost of the raw material plus the expense of purchasing resource time from outside the company to make the part is $250. The additional throughput generated is $50. When this is added to the total throughput for the company, the resulting throughput is $10,050 per week.

To make the decision the system needs to provide

- A view of the schedule including past due orders
- The part/operation to be unloaded
- The value of the sales order fed by the part/operation
- The total cost of the raw material involved

Using the System to Make the Decision

In Figure 9.5 orders 3 and 5 are late even though all efforts have been exhausted to maximize the utilization of the constraint. Sales order S/O111 can be either pushed into a future period, thereby relieving the constraint, or part/operation 123/30 can be off-loaded to a vendor.

If a decision is made to off-load to a vendor, purchasing can spend up to $200 in additional expense before throughput will be impacted negatively. Up to $199 and the company is generating more throughput.

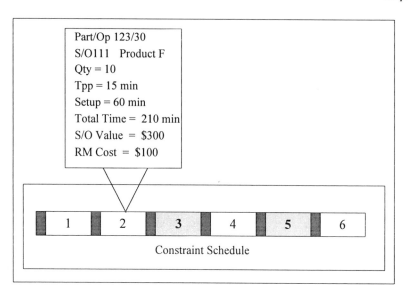

Figure 9.5   Off-loading to the vendor example data.

Off-Loading from Resources that Use Protective Capacity

One of the key issues in the previous discussion on the subordination process was the impact of conflicting orders. Whenever resources are loaded to the point where they are unable to respond effectively to the demands of the constraint and additional schedules must be created on secondary constraints, there is always the possibility that a conflict will exist between orders on the primary and secondary constraints.

In Figure 9.6 resource R-1 feeds resource R-2 and is loaded to 95%. R-2 is the capacity constrained resource and is loaded to 100%. Since R-1 feeds the CCR, its sole reason for existing is to provide R-2 with whatever it needs when it needs it. But R-1 does not have enough protective capacity to accomplish this task. Steps might be required to enhance its abilities by producing a schedule, combining setups or applying overtime. To do this, R-1 could be declared as a secondary constraint and a schedule created. If this is the case, the chances are good that conflicts will exist between orders scheduled on R-2 and those scheduled on R-1. When this occurs and everything possible has been done to increase its ability to deliver to the CCR on time but conflicts still exist, there are really only three alternatives: postpone the sales order, off-load the time to other resources or reduce the size of the rod or buffer which created the conflict.

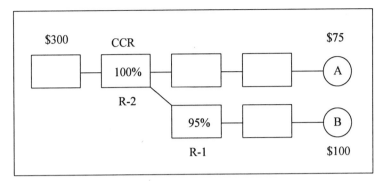

Figure 9.6   Another purchasing decision example.

When faced with this situation the system should identify all orders with rod or buffer conflicts and allow time for the decision to be made to either push the sales order into a later period, add temporary capacity or off-load. It should also determine the impact of the off-load by continuing the subordination process with the remaining orders as discussed in Chapter 7. If all of the current conflicts are resolved and no new ones are created, then the attempt was successful.

In some cases, off-loading to internal resources can cause additional problems. So a determination must be made whether to off-load demand from internal resources used to protect the constraint to an outside resource. How should this decision be made?

Figure 9.7 indicates that part/operations B and E are late due to rod violations. Notice that part/operation 4 has backward rods which extend toward part/operation B. Notice also that part/operation B is in violation of those rods. The rods are there to ensure that part/operation B has enough time to finish being processed on the secondary constraint before being sent to the primary constraint. In this case there is insufficient protection between the completion time of B and the start time of 4.

As mentioned earlier, there are three possible choices:

- Push part/operation 4 into the future to the full extent of the rods and delay the sales order.
- Find additional capacity for the secondary constraint.
- Shorten the backward rods from order 4.

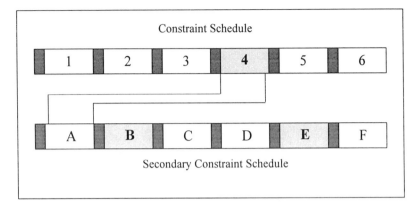

Figure 9.7   Constraint schedules showing rod violation.

Reducing the Size of the Rod

Rods can be reduced for selected orders when it is known that additional capacity is available, on a temporary basis, to help in the production of the conflicting order. Additional capacity can be added just prior to or when a specific order reaches the resource in question. In this case, another employee could be added to the secondary constraint for the processing of A and B and then removed when the problem has passed (see Figure 9.8).

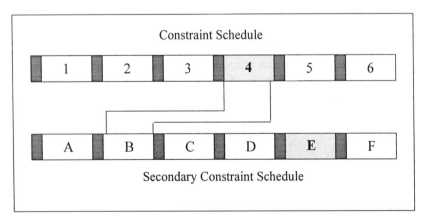

Figure 9.8   Constraint schedules showing reduction of rod size.

If additional capacity is not available to apply to the secondary constraint (whether for specific orders or in general) to solve the problem of conflicting orders, then perhaps outside capacity can help.

Off-Loading to the Vendor

If every possible alternative of finding additional internal capacity has been explored without success, then seeking an external source may be justified. There are two issues involved:

- The amount of throughput generated by the schedule when the order is delayed
- The amount of throughput generated when buying the processing time through an outside source

In Figure 9.9, part/operation A has been off-loaded to a vendor, resulting in an elimination of the rod violations for B and E. Part/operation 4 is no longer threatened, and as a result the sales order will not be pushed into the future.

To determine the impact to throughput the additional expense associated with off-loading to the vendor is added to the raw material cost to determine the total variable cost of the order. The total variable cost is then subtracted from the sales order to determine the throughput generated (see Figure 10).

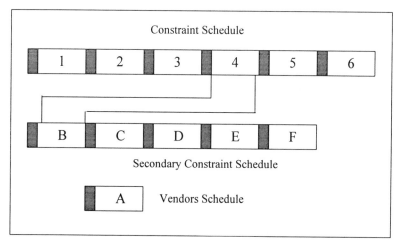

Figure 9.9 Constraint schedules showing off-loading to the vendor.

Farm out cost   Raw mat.   Total variable expense

$200   + $2000   = $2200

Sales price   Total exp.   Throughput

$3000   – $2200   = $800

Figure 9.10 Determining the throughput example.

Pushing the Order into the Future

When a sales order is pushed into the future due to a conflict between resources a new schedule is usually created for the constraint given the new due date for the sales order. When the constraint is rescheduled an attempt is again made to maximize its utilization. So the hole in the schedule created by pushing the new order into the future should no longer exist. Thus, the throughput generated by the constraint should not decline.

If the rescheduling process is not successful and a hole occurs in the schedule, throughput will decline (see Figure 9.11). If the reason is due to a conflict with an earlier resource such as in Figure 9.7, then the throughput generated using the additional expense of off-loading to the vendor needs to be compared to the estimated value of the unused CCR time. The estimated value of the unused CCR time is computed by multiplying the value per minute of the constraint times the total number of minutes taken by the hole. The value per minute of the constraint is the total sales generated by the schedule divided by the total time of the constraint used to generate the sales (see Figure 9.12).

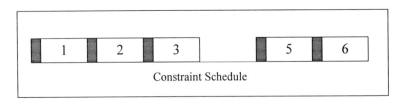

Figure 9.11 Holes in the schedule result in lower throughput.

$$\frac{\text{Total sales}}{\text{CCR time}} = \frac{\$300,000}{6000} = \$50/\text{min}$$

$$\text{Unused CCR time} = 30\text{min}$$

Estimated value of unused CCR time

$$30 \times \$50 = \$1500$$

Figure 9.12 Estimating the value of unused CCR time.

If the schedule for the constraint can be successfully rebuilt so that the hole no longer exists, then the issue in determining the impact of an off-load to a vendor is comparing the needs of the customer (having an on-time delivery) to the additional expense created by sending the order out. If there is an intolerant number of past due orders created on a consistent basis, then thought should be given to either elevating the constraint or increasing the amount of protective capacity on the secondary constraint so that conflicts are eliminated.

Note: after the constraint is rescheduled a second attempt is made to subordinate the remaining resources. If the sales orders involved in the conflict are pushed into the future by a full rod or buffer length, the same conflicts should not recur.

Off-Loading from Resources that Use Excess Capacity

Whenever excess capacity is present it should be recognized as unrealized throughput. In other words, there is value in the amount of throughput that could be generated by the excess capacity. If excess capacity is used to generate sales, the value of the order is considered the difference between the sales price and the cost of raw material. This can be a tremendous competitive edge and if it's not being used, someone should be attempting to identify how it could be.

However, to understand the impact of excess capacity on the purchasing decision some key questions should be answered:

- What is the impact of receiving material late on resources which have excess capacity?

- What is the impact of paying more for the part?
- Will receiving the part late create a temporary bottleneck? If so, what is the impact on those orders that go through resources which have the temporary bottleneck and are later processed on the constraint?

Normally, for those products which are processed entirely on resources where excess capacity is available and the part is delivered late, there is enough capacity to process the order and still deliver on time. If not, there will be enough capacity available at a later time to make up the difference in the total amount of throughput generated. The value of the raw material part to the company is less when excess capacity is involved. Since throughput is defined as the sales price minus the cost of raw material, paying more to obtain a part which is processed with excess capacity will result in an immediate decline in throughput.

Whenever raw material parts arrive late the effect is the same as shrinking the buffer. When the buffer is shrunk and parts are released later, the resource load is increased by having to accomplish the task in less time. This situation can create temporary bottlenecks threatening the constraint's ability to deliver on time. However, the normal buffer management system is designed to handle most late deliveries. For those parts which are processed on the constraint and go through resources which have a temporary bottleneck, priority should be given to those parts which create holes in the buffer (see Figure 9.13). Resource R-3 is shared by part/operations which feed sales orders S/O111 and S/O222. Only sales order S/O111 is fed by the constraint. Raw material part A is used exclusively on S/O111 and raw material part B is used only on S/O222.

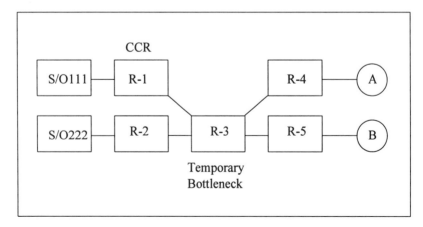

Figure 9.13 Purchasing decision with bottleneck in schedule.

Due to a problem in delivery from the vendor, Part A was released late for processing on R-4 and now, since B arrived first, A must wait until B is finished processing. This is a temporary condition. In other words, the total available capacity on resource R-4 is more than enough to fill the needs of protecting the constraint. However, because A was late R-4 is temporarily required to exceed its capability. Since this is physically impossible, a delay in the arrival of A to the constraint is imminent. If the delay is long enough that it begins to threaten zone I of the buffer at R-1, then part A will be expedited, thereby alleviating the situation. In this case paying more for the part that feeds the non-constraint resources, which uses excess capacity so that parts will arrive on time, up to a point, is a waste. At what point should the additional expense be approved?

The buffer management system discussed in Chapter 8 is used to manage the situation where normal fluctuations in the production process occur during execution of the schedule. However, by looking at the release schedule for raw material a decision can be made earlier in the process, when it is known that there is a high probability that a specific delivery date will cause a problem.

Figure 9.14 is a raw material requirements schedule. Included in the schedule are

- Part number and description of the part required
- Gating operation and resource where the part is to be released

Late Raw Material Requirements Schedule						
Part No.	Description	Gating Op./ Resource	Buffer/ Size	Release Date	Due Date	% Buffer
12345	**Armature**	**123/30/R-7**	**C/5 Days**	**154**	**158**	**80%**
12369	**Gasket**	**124/30/R-7**	**C/5 Days**	**154**	**157**	**60%**
45783	Flight Line	234/40/R-6	A/5 Days	153	155	40%
27240	Sky Hook	456/30/R-8	S/5 Days	152	153	20%

Figure 9.14 Late raw material requirements schedule.

- Buffer size for the buffer origin that the specific part/operation feeds
- Scheduled release date at the gating operation
- Due date of the purchase order required to fill the requirement
- Percentage of the buffer taken

Notice that this report is in descending sequence based on the amount of buffer taken by the late delivery. Raw material part 12345 for gating operation 123/30 resource R-7 is scheduled to be released at day 154 and feeds a 5 day buffer for the constraint. However, it is not scheduled to arrive from the vendor until day 158 and has taken 80% of the buffer in front of the constraint. In this case the part must be expedited. Part 27240 is going to be late, but it takes only 20% of the shipping buffer. In this case the part does not justify spending additional money to expedite.

Note: under the "Buffer/size" column, the constraint, shipping and assembly buffers are designated C, S and A, respectively. For example, "A/5 Days" means a 5 day assembly buffer.

SALES AND MARKETING

The TOC based information system can have a very large impact to the sales and marketing department. When the impact of the TOC approach is compared to the traditional method the difference is quite noticeable. Poor scheduling methods and cost accounting have caused major problems for these two organizations. The information system will be discussed with the following tasks in mind:

- Selling the right product mix
- Quoting delivery dates
- Changes in the schedule
- Accepting orders
- Developing new markets
- Selling excess capacity

Selling the Right Product Mix

Selling the right product mix can have a tremendous impact on profitability, yet most companies do not have the slightest idea of how to perform this task. This is not surprising considering most people have been taught incorrectly for the last 50 or more years. In addition, there are very few information systems being sold in the world today which can help to perform this task. Without rehashing the decision process, what is needed to make decisions is a comparison of the throughput generated per unit of the constraint for the products being sold.

What the information system must provide to determine the right product mix to sell into the market is

- The identity of the constraint
- The amount of time each product absorbs from the constraint
- The sales price of each product
- The raw material cost

Most systems today can provide the last two ingredients. Because of the problems discussed in Chapter 2, few systems can provide the first two. Once the constraint has been identified, what is needed is a method for calculating the total time for all part/operations which cross the constraint and belong to a specific product. It is a simple task to create a list of products with their respective throughput per unit of the constraint figures in descending order, the top being the most profitable and the bottom the least (see Figure 9.15). Product A is the most profitable, with $10.00 per minute, followed by B with $8.00. D is the least profitable. When setting sales strategies and commission schedules this information is vital and should be readily available from the information system.

Product	Sales Price	Raw Material	Throughput Generated	Total CCR Time	T/uc
A	300	150	150	15	$10.00
B	310	150	160	20	$8.00
C	200	100	100	15	$6.67
D	400	150	250	45	$5.56

Figure 9.15 Determining the right product mix—example data.

When Labor Is the Constraint

Companies will often assume that a constraint is a physical resource or machine in the factory and that it is constantly moving from resource to resource depending on product mix. To adapt, employees are trained to handle numerous jobs so that when the constraint moves the work force can be adjusted to fit the new environment. When the number of employees are no longer able to meet the demand by switching from resource to resource, the available labor generated by employees becomes the constraint. This circumstance is rarely observed correctly. Companies will usually continue in the attempt to move employees as the constraint moves, not realizing that the constraint is actually the number of production people available.

Determining product mix in this environment is very similar to the way in which it is calculated when the physical constraint is a machine. The amount of time used by the constraint is divided into the amount of throughput generated. The difference is that the constraint is the total employee time required to produce the product. Figure 9.16 is similar to 9.15 in that the products, sales prices, raw material costs and throughput are the same. However, notice that the time used for the constraint has increased to the include total labor required to produce the product. Notice also that the order of the most profitable product has changed. Product C is now the most profitable, while product B is the least. Whenever the constraint changes there will probably be a change in product mix.

Product	Sales Price	Raw Material	Throughput Generated	Total Labor	T/uc
A	300	150	150	60	$2.50
B	310	150	160	120	$1.33
C	200	100	100	30	$3.33
D	400	150	250	90	$2.78

Figure 9.16 Product mix data showing the total labor required per product.

Note: it has never been the constraint's obligation to tell anyone that it has moved.

When Raw Material Is the Constraint

Sometimes the constraint will surface in the form of raw material. In other words, there will not be enough of a specific part to build all of the requirements of the market. In Figure 9.17 raw material part A is contained in products F, I, H and G. There is a limit to the number of As available to fill the market for these products. To compute the throughput per unit of the constraint, the number of parts required for each product is divided into the throughput generated for the product. In this case, product F is the most profitable. It generates $300 in throughput each time one is sold and it takes 3 part As to create each one. The throughput per unit of the constraint is therefore $100.

Accepting Orders

The key factor in accepting a sales order is identifying what the lowest amount of throughput per unit of the constraint that is being sold now. As an example, if the constraint is being sold for $6.00 per minute now (by definition it has no additional capacity), to accept an order at less than $6.00 a minute would decrease the profit of the company. In Figure 9.15, if all the constraint's time were spent processing products A, B and C, processing D would cause profit to immediately decline.

Raw Material Constraint:		A	
Product	Throughput	Req/Unit	T/uc
F	$300	3	$100
I	$100	1	$100
H	$150	2	$75
G	$200	3	$66

Figure 9.17 Product mix example data.

To make this decision the salesman needs to know:

- The amount of throughput per unit that would be generated from the product being sold
- The lowest throughput per unit of the constraint that is being sold now

Salesmen should go into the field knowing these two facts and management should ensure that they are provided.

Quoting Delivery Dates

When quoting a delivery date for products that go through the constraint the salesman only needs to look at the constraint schedule for open time on the horizon in which to fit the order. For a precise schedule, the system should allow the processing of sales quotes that could load the system with data as if it were a valid order and have it process the new delivery date based on the additional data. (This requires a different system structure, which will be discussed in Chapter 11.)

If the salesman is selling excess capacity, it is important not to create temporary bottlenecks on the non-constraint resources which will threaten the constraint. It would still be necessary to load the quoted order on the system to arrive at a precise delivery date.

Changes in the Schedule

There are two schedule-related conditions under which a change in order due date will occur:

- Those changes which happen in the schedule and are predicted beforehand
- Those that occur as a result of problems which create holes in the buffer

When changes occur in the schedule due to conflicts between resources or a lack of adequate protection, this information is immediately fed back to the master schedule. Because of this feedback mechanism, a salesman can be made aware of these conditions immediately and is able to make priority decisions on which orders should actually slip (see Figure 9.18). Order 2 (connected to sales order S/O111) and order 4 (connected to sales order S/O222) are on the constraint

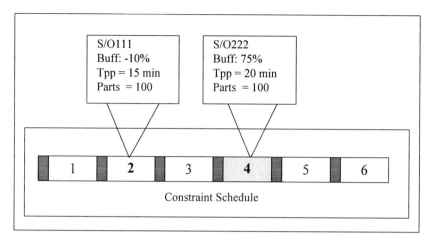

Figure 9.18 Information of schedule changes aids decision-making.

schedule. Order 4 is going to be late because it has taken 75% of its buffer time. Order 2 is actually early; it has an additional 10% of the buffer length in front of it. If re-scheduled to a later time, sales order S/O222 will probably be pushed so that the full buffer in front of order 4 is recovered. If the length of the buffer is estimated to be 2 days, the customer can be notified that the order will be 1½ days late.

However, what if the customer for sales order S/O222 could not really afford to have the order postponed and the customer for sales order S/O111 could? By giving order 4 priority over order 2, 150 minutes of constraint time can be recovered and given to order 4 along with part of order 2's buffer (see Figure 9.19). The buffer for order 4 was partially restored while the buffer for order 2 is now at 50%.

As discussed earlier, orders which cause holes in the buffer for zone I will be given a higher priority over those which are on time. This priority is given by having the offending order expedited. If during the expedite phase it is discovered that the order will definitely not meet the shipping schedule, then the sales department should be notified immediately and feedback given to the customer.

Note: it is better to tell the customer early that an order will be late rather than waiting until it is already late.

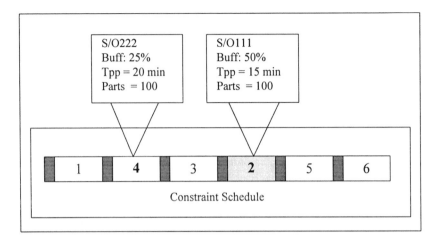

Figure 9.19 Rescheduling done due to changes in the schedule.

Setting the new ship date depends on where in the process the order is and how far it must travel before getting to shipping. If the order is being expedited, it will take less time than the normal buffer length to reach the buffer origin. If the buffer is for the constraint, there may be additional capacity afterwards so that the order may still reach shipping on time.

When a problem occurs on R-5 in Figure 9.20, causing a hole in the buffer for R-3, and it is actually late leaving the constraint, there is also the buffer in front of shipping to consider.

The maximum that an order should take is one shipping buffer after leaving the constraint. The actual due date given the customer is based on the experience of

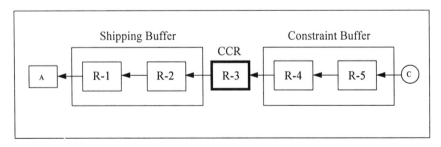

Figure 9.20 Schedule changes can also affect the shipping buffer.

the buffer manager in judging how long it will take to process from a given operation.

Once an initial due date is determined it can be validated by placing the new due date into the system and creating a new schedule.

Note: in creating the alternative schedule, the original schedule should not be changed. Provisions should be made to copy the original schedule and modify it to determine if the new schedule is reliable. By changing the old schedule, the order would not appear as late and, therefore, would not be expedited (see Chapter 11).

Selling Excess Capacity

For sales, the absence of an internal constraint is usually an indication that a policy constraint is blocking them from pulling the physical constraint inside the company. However, the presence of a physical constraint does not indicate that all excess capacity has been located and a plan developed to exploit it. Before excess capacity can be sold management must know

- Where the excess capacity is
- How much of it is available
- What products are impacted

Excess capacity cannot be found based on the amount of idle time recorded at any given resource. Since the scheduling process involves all resources within the throughput chain, what appears as excess capacity at one resource may actually be capacity used to protect another. In Figure 9.21 resource R-1 is the constraint and is loaded to 100%. It will obviously have difficulty delivering to the sales order more often than a resource which is loaded to 80%.

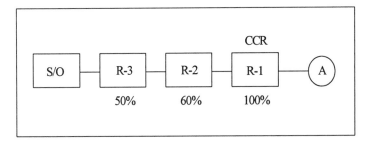

Figure 9.21 Selling excess capacity example.

However, it is not just resource R-1's effort which is involved. If the order is late leaving the constraint, resources R-2 and R-3 have additional capacity to devote to alleviating the situation. In a chain of resources one resource cannot be judged individually. Their performance must be judged as a team.

Note: a throughput chain involves all resources which are connected from the vendor to the market by the process of generating throughput.

If a string of resources has the capability to deliver to the market more than the market is willing to buy, then there must be excess capacity. This is a key issue. The question is, how much additional capacity is there and how should it be used? When the constraint is in the market, the system will attempt to subordinate to the schedule created by the sales orders. When the system can no longer accomplish this task without increasing capacity on an internal resource (exploitation), then the company is no longer selling excess capacity for that throughput chain.

Looking for New Markets

The TOC based system can simulate reality so well that capacity simulations can easily spot where additional resource availability can be found for certain products and where others will create conflicts. If in the process of determining how to break a certain marketing constraint new products are proposed, the impact of the new products and how they will affect the internal capabilities of the manufacturing resources can be re-created. Mock bills of material, routings and a forecast can be used to simulate the new load even before the products are designed.

Note: if one throughput chain has a capacity constrained resource (CCR), it does not mean all throughput chains within the company have one. If there is no excess capacity in one area of the company, look in another.

FINANCE AND ACCOUNTING

Throughput Justification

One of the biggest advantages of using the TOC based system for finance and accounting is the ability to really examine requests for capital expenditures. Since cost accounting has major flaws in this area (e.g., cost justification), the need for this kind of tool in justifying spending is quite large.

Cost Justification for an MRP System			
Inventory Value	$10,000,000		Savings
Decreased Inventory	20%	Inventory	$160,000/yr
Carrying Cost	8%	Labor	$65,000/yr
Cost Reduction	$160,000/yr		
Labor Cost/Inventory Management	$150,000/yr	**Total Savings**	**$225,000/yr**
Increased Efficiency	10%	**Investment**	**$500,000**
Cost Reduction	$15,000/yr		
		Break Even	**2.2 yr**
Labor Cost/Production	$1,000,000/yr		
Increased Efficiency	5%		
Cost Reduction	$50,000/yr		

Figure 9.22   Cost justification for MRP system based on labor savings.

In cost justification the objective is to justify an expense based on the amount of cost that is reduced. Seldom is the actual cost reduction ever realized. As an example, whenever a justification is made for the purposes of buying the traditional information system it is usually based, at least partly, on the increase in the efficiency of employees. This increase in efficiency is converted to labor savings and presented as a reduction in cost (see Figure 9.22).

Unfortunately, this labor savings is almost never realized. Instead, the company pays for the system, which increases the money leaving the company and never has a layoff to offset for the increase in expenses. Additionally, because of the problems discussed earlier, MRP can have a damaging impact on the scheduling of the factory. If an increase in rate at which inventory is consumed does not occur, then inventory may not decline. In fact, it may even go up.

In order to justify spending money the justification must be based on the increase in throughput generated by the expense. Justifications can fall into three categories:

1. Those used to exploit or elevate the constraint
2. Those used to increase protective capacity
3. Those used to increase excess capacity

The first category will obviously result in throughput being increased. When the amount of increase in throughput due to the change is compared to the cost of the change, a real payback figure can be obtained (see Figure 9.23). The additional throughput generated is estimated to be $10,000 per month due to the improvement. The cost of the improvement is $60,000 and the payback period is 6 months. This is the minimum information needed by the finance department when justifying an expenditure and should be requested from all departments when submitting.

Creating the Throughput Justification
(Improving Without Breaking the Constraint)

In creating the throughput justification for improvements to an internal capacity constrained resource the key issues to understand are

- How much additional capacity will be generated on the constraint by making the improvement
- What will be done with the additional capacity

By definition, unless the constraint is broken, there will always be more market available than productive capability. However, if sales is doing its job, those products which create the highest throughput per unit of the constraint will be limited by the market and not the capacity constrained resource.

Additional Throughput Generated	$10,000/mo.
Cost of Improvement	$60,000
Payback	6 mo.

Figure 9.23   Throughput justification measurements.

		Resource R-4			
Product	T/uc	Time/unit	Qty	Total Time	New Time/Unit
M	$10.00	20 min	120	2400	10
N	$6.66	45 min	37	1665	45
L	$5.55	90 min	5	450	90
O	$3.33	30 min	8	240	30

Figure 9.24 Throughput justification—redistributing processing time.

If multiple products are being scheduled on the constraint and one is more profitable than the others, marketing's objective should be to sell all the available constraint time for the most profitable product until it has reached the marketing constraint for that product. Once reached, the additional capacity should be taken by products which are of less value. So, in trying to determine how much additional throughput will be generated by an improvement, the additional throughput will, more than likely, be originating from those products which are less profitable.

In Figure 9.24, R-4 is the capacity constrained resource. R-4 processes products L through O and is loaded with 4755 minutes for a ten week period. Product M is the most profitable at $10 per minute of constraint time, while product O is the least profitable at $3.33 per minute. Notice that, after an improvement has been made in R-4's capability, the processing time for product M has dropped from 20 minutes to 10 minutes per unit under the new time column. This means that the 120 units of product M now take 1200 minutes to make instead of the original 2400. The question is, what should be done with the additional 1200 minutes released from the constraint?

All of the available market for products M, N and L should have been already sold or an order would not have been accepted for product O. Since the basis of the example was to improve the constraint and not to break it, there should be more market for product O than available capacity. In justifying an expenditure for increasing capacity on resource R-4, all 1200 minutes of additional capacity created by reducing the amount of time taken to produce M would be absorbed by selling additional Os. Throughput for a minute of the constraint for selling and producing product O is $3.33. Multiplied by the additional capacity released (1200 minutes), the additional throughput generated is $3,996 for the ten week period. If the investment is $10,000, it would take approximately six months to break even.

If a marketing constraint is encountered prior to reaching the end of the additional 1200 minutes, then the physical constraint for R-4 has been broken and a new constraint must be identified and included in the justification of the $10,000 investment. Since the constraint has been broken, a new product mix must be established before any throughput estimate can be made. However, it may be that part of the justification will include the introduction of a new product which will absorb the remaining constraint time and leave R-4 as the primary constraint.

Breaking the Constraint

In breaking the constraint the change in the company can become quite complex and have major implications. Key issues in determining the impact include the following:

- If the constraint is to be broken, where will it go next and what will be the impact on the current load in the factory?
- How much will throughput go up based on the current demand?
- What list of products will now become the most profitable based on throughput per unit of the constraint?
- Will any new conflicts develop between other resources?
- Can an effective schedule be created given the change?
- Will the constraint be pushed into another department or possibly into the market? If so, what will be the impact?

To answer these kinds of questions will take an information system with the ability to simulate the change. Fortunately, while the change may be complex, the process to be performed never changes. The objective should be to implement the five steps given the new data.

The first issue is to make the change in the data used by the system and see where the new constraint might go. Once identified, the remainder of the five steps must be implemented. After completion, the impact of the change can be determined and the justification either approved or disapproved.

Increasing Protective Capacity

If the request is to facilitate subordination by increasing the amount of protective capacity available, one of two situations should exist:

- A persistent conflict between two resources which has gone unresolved and results in continuously rescheduling sales orders to later time periods
- Holes in the buffer which can be directly attributed to a specific problem

In solving conflicts which result in orders being pushed into later time periods, the justification is made based on the value of the sales dollars pushed. For those situations where a specific problem results in constantly expediting material due to holes developing in zone I of the buffer, the justification is made based on the amount of inventory or operating expense reduced as a result of being able to shrink the buffer due to the change.

Increasing Excess Capacity

The third situation is usually presented by the person who does not have experience or knowledge of TOC. The justification is usually based on the amount of time saved by not doing a specific activity. While these can usually be dismissed quickly, they are an indication that someone in the organization needs some training. Unless there is a valid plan to use the excess capacity to increase throughput the request should be turned down.

Cash Flow Management

Having a valid schedule with predictable results means being able to effectively manage cash flow. This is extremely important for companies that are having problems in this area. The system can be used to predict the rate at which money enters and leaves the company so that better projections can be made. By simply assigning a throughput value to each sales order, the schedule will produce a forecast of the rate in which money enters the company. Notice that if labor and overhead are removed from the current cost accounting system, the cost of goods sold is now the cost of raw material. Subtract that figure from the sales price and the result is the throughput figure for the company. Notice that this figure will also be the profit margin on most traditional systems.

A raw material receipt schedule along with the current operating expense plus the overtime projected by the system will identify the cash needed to operate the company. Operating expense can be adjusted based on the additional overtime required by the schedule.

The result is a complete picture of how and when money enters and leaves the company for the planning horizon.

QUALITY ASSURANCE

The constraint should be fully utilized in generating throughput. From a quality perspective this means

- Parts processed by the constraint should not be delayed by rework.
- After being processed on the constraint parts should not be scrapped.

Minimizing inventory and operating expense means reducing the problems which prevent the reduction of protective capacity (those things which create holes in zone I of the buffer).

In addition to identifying the constraint and providing the buffer management process, the system should supply an idea of how resources interface. In other words, which part/operations and resources:

- Feed the constraint
- Are diverging
- Are converging
- Appear after the constraint

Trying to produce product flow diagrams to define these issues can be a tedious effort and will probably require changing as soon as the ink is dry on the first set. Two visual tools supplied by the information system can help tremendously in this effort. They include the "where used" and "descending part/operations" screens.

The Where Used and Descending Part/Operations Screens

These screens are actually visual representations of the net. The descending part/operations screen starts at the sales order and presents all part/operations

Descending	Where used	
S/O111 - A	RM C	
A/ 30 R-1	B/ 10	R-6
A/ 20 R-2	B/ 20	R-5
A/ 10 R-3	B/ 30	**R-4**
B/ 30 **R-4**	A/ 10	R-3
B/ 20 R-5	A/ 20	R-2
B/ 10 R-6	A/ 30	R-1
RM C	S/O111 - A	

Figure 9.25   Descending part/operations and where used screens.

and the resources on which a specific sales order is to be processed. The where used screen starts at the raw material and traces upward through all part operations and resources to all sales orders which may be using the part (see Figure 9.25).

Notice that the constraint appears in bold. If there is a problem which exists on a resource prior to or after the constraint such as a capability index (Cpk) of 1.00 on resource R-5 part/operation B/20, it is easy to see that B/20 feeds the constraint and that a low Cpk could cause some serious problems for the constraint's ability to perform. It is also easy to see that if any scrap occurs on part/operations B/30 through A/30, the loss would be the price of the entire sales order. In addition, if there is a problem in receiving a particular purchase order on time or if there is a quality problem which effects raw material part C, the where used screen can identify the part/operations and sales orders that are impacted.

An abbreviated version of these screens includes those part/operations and resources which appear after the constraint and feed the sales order (the "red lane") as well as those part/operations and resources that feed the constraint (see Figure 9.26).

A modification of the descending part/operation and where used screens includes the addition of some important indicators (see Figure 9.27). Notice that

Figure 9.26 The red lane and resources feeding the constraint can be generated from descending part/operations and where used screens.

rework and downtime information only appears for resources R-2 and R-4. To place this information on the system would only cause confusion if there is capacity available to handle these issues. Additionally, if there were a problem on these resources, it would appear in buffer management. The objective of this screen is to point the activity toward those resources which have critical capacity shortages. Scrap appears only for those resources that go from the constraint to the end of the process (the red lane).

Throughput Chain 1

PRODUCT A		PRODUCT B	
PRODUCT C			
Resource	Scrap	Rework	Down-time
R-1	.01		
S **R-2**	.05	.10	.07
R-3	.00		
P **R-4**	.02	.03	.05
R-5			
R-6			

Figure 9.27 Key indicators of modified descending part/operations and where used screens.

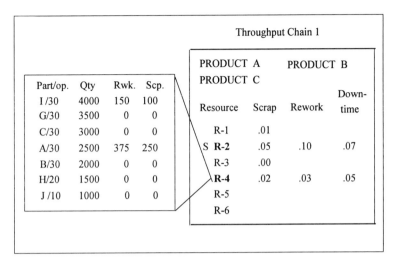

Figure 9.28 Detailed information available from screen shown in Figure 9.27.

These are important keys in focusing the quality program. But additional information is still needed, such as on what part/operations the scrap or rework is occurring (see Figure 9.28). Part/operations I/30 and A/30 are absorbing all of the scrap or rework time.

Making the Scrap or Rework Decision: Re-Visiting the Quality Decision

A decision which can involve both production and the quality organization is how to know when to scrap or rework a part. Using the traditional methods will not work. Figure 9.29 shows the data required to make the decision and can

PRODUCT	CCR TIME/UNIT	CCR TIME AVAIL.
A	15	1500 min
ORDER = 100	SP = $100	RM = $25
DEFECTIVE PARTS	TIME/UNIT	MATERIAL
10	10	$5

Figure 9.29 Scrap versus rework example data.

serve as a basis for what features might be required for the information system to help in this process.

As previously indicated, product A takes 15 minutes to process on the CCR and uses $25 in raw material for each part produced. An order of 100 is being processed at a sales price of $100 each. After 50% of the order has been processed, 10 parts are found to be defective. It will take an additional $5 in raw material and 10 minutes of constraint time to repair each one. The question is should the 10 parts be scrapped or reworked?

If the 10 parts are to be scrapped, then they will need to be replaced to fill the order. 60 additional parts are to be processed creating throughput of $(100 - 25)$ $75 each for a total throughput generated of $4,500. Since each part takes 15 minutes of constraint time and there are 60 parts, the total constraint time consumed will be 900 minutes. To replace the raw material scrapped for each of the 10 parts, $250 must be subtracted from the total throughput generated. To scrap and replace the 10 parts and process the remaining order will take 900 minutes and generate $4,250, or $4.72 per minute of constraint time (see Figure 9.30).

To rework the 10 parts requires an additional $5 raw material be subtracted from the sales price $(100 - 30)$, which will generate $70 of throughput for each of the 10 parts processed for a total throughput of $700. It will take 100 minutes of constraint time to process all 10 parts. The remaining 50 parts will take 750 minutes of constraint time and generate $3,750, for a total of $4,450 generated with 850 minutes of constraint time, or $5.23 per minute (see Figure 9.31). The

			(T)	CCR TIME
THROUGHPUT	=	$60(100 - 25)$ =	$4,500	900
MATERIAL	=	10×25 =	$ 250	
			$4,250	900

$$T/uc = \frac{\$4,250}{900} = \$4.72$$

Figure 9.30 Scrap versus rework example—calculations for scrap and replace.

			(T)	CCR TIME
THROUGHPUT	=	10 (100 – 30) =	$700	100
THROUGHPUT	=	50 (100 – 25) =	$3,750	750
			$4,450	850

$$T/uc = \frac{\$4,450}{850} = \$5.23$$

Figure 9.31 Scrap versus rework example—calculations for rework.

throughput per minute of the constraint for the rework is greater, so the choice from the data given would be to rework the parts.

The decision can be made with much less data than given. Once the parts causing the problem have been processed on the constraint, the question becomes how to maximize the throughput of the system given the current situation. The first issue is that the parts must be replaced so that the sales order can be delivered. At first glance it will take $5.00 of additional raw material and 10 minutes of the constraints time to generate $100 for each part if the parts are reworked. If they are scrapped, it will take an additional $25 of raw material and 15 minutes of constraint time to make the $100. Throughput per unit of the constraint for rework is $9.50. Throughput per unit of the constraint for scrap is $5.00 (see Figure 9.32). The only data necessary to make the decision are:

			(T)	CCR TIME
THROUGHPUT	=	10 (100 – 5) =	$950	100
THROUGHPUT	=	10 (100 – 25) =	$750	150

Rework Scrap

$$T/uc = \frac{\$950}{100} = \$9.50 \qquad T/uc = \frac{\$750}{150} = \$5.00$$

Figure 9.32 Scrap versus rework example—calculations using TOC data.

				T/uc
Part/Operation	A/30	Scrap:		$5.00
		Rework:		$9.50
CCR Time Est. (Rework)	10			
		Product:		A
Add. Raw material (Rework)	$5.00	Sales Order:		S/O111

Figure 9.33   Providing information for making the scrap/rework decision.

- The original cost of raw material for the product
- The sales price of the order
- An estimate of the amount of additional raw material and constraint time required to repair
- The quantity of the parts to be reworked or scrapped
- The original constraint time for the part

The question now is what can the system do to provide this kind of information? Figure 9.33 represents an interactive screen which can be created to help with the scrap/rework decision. The only data needed to enter are the part/operations being considered, the estimated constraint time to repair and the additional raw material required. Additional data, such as the sales price of the order, the original constraint time and the original raw material cost, can be obtained from the manufacturing system data base.

The impact of scrap and rework on the scheduling process

Whenever a scrap or rework occurs there will be an impact on the amount of labor and material required by the system. This must be reflected in the scheduling process. Figure 9.34 is a product flow diagram for product A, which has a sales order demand for 10 units. The numbers appearing between each part/operation are the bill of material relationships. Notice that for A/30 to be processed it must receive one A/20 from resource R-2. Notice also that resource R-2 scraps 25% of the A/20s it creates. This means that for every A/30 created, 1.33 A/20s must be processed first. To process 1.33 units of A/20, R-2 must receive 1.33 units of A/10. To produce all 10 units of A on the sales order requires 13.3 units of raw material C.

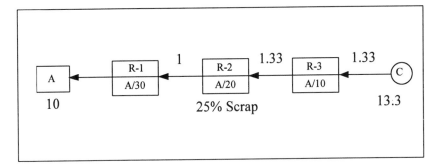

Figure 9.34 The impact of scrap on the scheduling process.

Scrap affects not only material requirements, but resource requirements as well. In order to obtain 1 unit of A/20 to be transferred to A/30, resources R-2 and R-3 must process the additional material. Additional processing will obviously take more resource time. This kind of processing must be considered when creating the net and in determining the load. It is done by modifying the bill of material relationship during processing.

Rework is considered somewhat differently than scrap. Scrap is simply yielded during processing. However, rework will usually require a modification of the net (see Figure 9.35). Notice that 25% of all A/10s are reworked back to the beginning of the process. This means a certain increase in the load for resources R-3, R-4 and R-5. It will also mean an adaptation of the rods, provided a constraint schedule is involved, to insure that reworked material maintains a specific distance in time from the process time of the original parts.

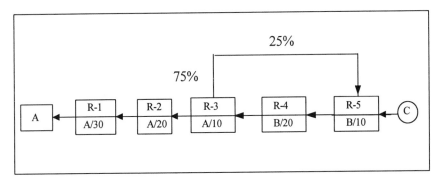

Figure 9.35 The impact of rework on the scheduling process.

ENGINEERING

As described in *The Next Phase of Total Quality Management*, the focusing mechanisms provided by the traditional methods such as

- Single minute exchange of die (SMED)
- Total productive maintenance (TPM)
- Statistical process control (SPC)
- Design of experiments (DOE)
- Quality function deployment

lack an effective mechanism for focusing activity so that the use of the tool is in line with the goal of the company. The TOC based information system can provide that focus. From a physical perspective, the task of determining what to fix and when to fix it is made easy.

To increase throughput these tools should focus on the constraint(s). To decrease inventory and operating expense they should be focused on those things which consistently create holes in zone I of the buffer. However, it is not enough just to know that a reduction in setup time will increase throughput. The question that should be asked is how can engineering minimize the amount of time spent in setup or machine downtime in the generation of throughput.

Setup Reduction

Figure 9.36 is a Pareto analysis of the setup time for those part/operations which cross the constraint. By pinpointing those part/operations that take the most time from the schedule to perform setup, engineering's time can be better focused to maximize the generation of throughput.

Resource R-4 is the primary constraint, with 7000 minutes total demand. After having completed the schedule generation to include setup reduction, the amount of run time available to generate throughput is 86% of the total time available. This means the constraint is losing 14% of its productive capability to setup. Notice that 30% of the 1000 minutes is being used for part/operation E/30. By concentrating on reducing the setup requirements on part/operation E/30 and making significant reductions, engineering will return more throughput for their effort.

An additional consideration is the volume of setups performed. If E/30 takes 30% of all setup time on the schedule but only one order is involved, the oppor-

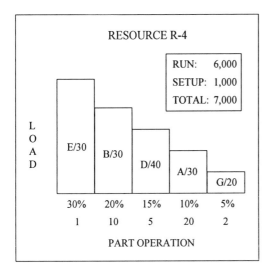

Figure 9.36 Setup reduction.

tunity for improvement may be less than for part/operation B/30 which includes 10 setups. Notice that under each percentage in the figure the number of setups involved is also shown.

Note: a high number of setups also indicates that setup savings may be extended to cover more orders.

Total Productive Maintenance

As seen in *The Next Phase of Total Quality Management*, total productive maintenance (TPM) has some serious problems in attempting to focus on the right areas of the company. Like most cost based focusing mechanisms, TPM uses local measurements without considering that the resources involved are somehow connected to one another. The TPM effectiveness rating is comprised of the measurements of availability, efficiency and quality:

$$\text{Effectiveness} = \text{availability} \times \text{efficiency} \times \text{quality}$$

Each resource is measured in this fashion regardless of where it is in the overall throughput chain or what the characteristics of the individual resource might be.

Figure 9.37 Re-focusing total productive maintenance.

To be effective, the individual measurements of availability, efficiency and quality must be placed in the context of the way in which resources interface. In other words, what are the relationships between resources and how do the individual measurements help in determining where to focus specific efforts to improve? (See Figure 9.37.)

Notice that resource R-3 is in bold and that availability, efficiency and quality ratings are shown. R-3 has been identified as the constraint. Notice also that the chain of resources leading from R-3 to the finished product have quality ratings. The objective for this screen is to identify for the engineer where to place efforts to maximize the amount of throughput generated. To do this, availability, efficiency and quality should be maximized on the constraint. Quality must be maximized to prevent scrap on the string of resources leading to the finished product. Additional information provided in the window to the left includes the part/operations which cross the constraint.

Note: to improve on the remaining resources buffer management is used so that the impact of the problems encountered on the non-constraints can be aggregated.

Product Design

Whenever efforts are necessary to improve the amount of throughput generated by the constraint, a key issue in releasing the maximum amount of constraint time for the effort given is to design products so that they actually take less

			Time/	Units
STN	PROD	T/ uc	Unit	Produced
I / 30	I	10.00	0:30	4000
G/ 30	G	9.00	0:45	3500
C/ 30	C	15.00	0:20	3000
A/ 30	A	8.50	0:25	2500
B/ 30	B	14.00	0:30	2000
H/ 20	H	6.00	0:45	1500
J/ 10	J	7.00	0:45	1000

Resource R-4

Figure 9.38 Support for engineering.

constraint time. Figure 9.38 shows a listing of all part/operations which cross the constraint, the product produced, the throughput per unit, the amount of time it takes to produce each product, and the number of units to be produced on the schedule.

Notice that the chart is listed in descending order based on the total number of parts to be produced on the constraint. For each minute saved in producing product I, 4000 minutes of constraint time will be released to sell into the market. The question then becomes what products should be sold given the additional 4000 minutes. This, of course, is a marketing issue.

PRODUCTION

Like every department within the company, the decisions made by production should be based on those actions required to implement the five-step process of improvement. Decisions should obviously be made in the context of where in the process production is. If the constraint is in the market, then the actions required will be different than if the constraint is on a particular resource within the plant. The first step, regardless of where it is currently located, is to identify the constraint and then subordinate the actions of the other departments.

With one exception, most of the decision support for production has been applied in the creation of the schedule and control portions of the system. This includes:

- Setup savings
- Order priority
- Overtime
- Expediting
- Head count requirements
- Off-loading

The system prompts the user at certain times to make decisions regarding the task being performed. As an example, when the constraint has been identified and the first step in the exploitation process has been accomplished a schedule exists which includes a list of orders with start and stop dates for specific part/operations across the constraint. What also exists is an indication of what orders will be late unless changes are made. The decision of how to fix the late orders may include setup savings, off-loading of orders or overtime.

During the scheduling process the system offers an opportunity to perform any of these tasks and will demonstrate the outcome through simulating the interactions between the resources as a result of the decision. However, it does not indicate which should be done first or in what order. This should be a management decision.

The preferred method of presentation for the schedule as well as a model for the decision process is graphical. The system will present orders from the schedule on a time line for the constraint being exploited. It will show which orders are on time and which will be late based on color or, as in Figure 9.39, by using a pattern. In the figure, orders 1 and 4 are indicating that they will be late. The determination is made by the amount of buffer still remaining in front of the order. If an order has less than half the buffer remaining, it is considered a problem order and will be late. A decision must be made to determine the best way to exploit the resource.

Figure 9.39   Schedule presentation.

When making a decision which affects the exploitation process, a certain pecking order is indicated by the impact to profitability. Setup savings should be tried first. It is the cheapest way to increase capacity. Next comes off-loading, then overtime, and, as a last resort, postponing certain sales orders.

However, each decision cannot be made in a vacuum and must be tempered by the situation. As an example, the system has no way of knowing that part of the data it may be using are wrong. If an indication is made by the system that a conflict exists between the primary and secondary constraint and off-loading should be considered, the system may not know that the particular resource needed for off-loading is broken and that the alternative decision to push sales order due dates may be a better solution. Additionally, the system can indicate which orders are going to be late as a result of the conflict and is able to relate the new due date of the sales order, but it can't understand which customer orders should be postponed at the expense of others. This is why human intervention is necessary during certain steps in the scheduling process.

Off-Loading

To aid in the off-loading of orders the system should provide a method of determining which alternative resources are available so that when making the off-load decision, possible selections will be readily available (see Figure 9.40). What the system can offer is alternatives. And because it resembles reality so well, it can simulate the impact on throughput, inventory and operating expense as a result of the decision.

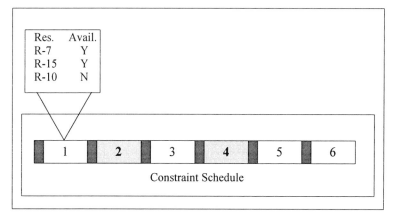

Figure 9.40 Off-loading constraint schedule alternative.

Note: using the system to make decisions based on the outcome of certain simulation attempts is a poor management strategy and should be avoided. Simulation should be used only after good decisions are made to validate them.

SUMMARY

Making the day-to-day decisions for running a business can have a major impact on how well the company performs. When the results of those decisions are in line with the goal of the company profits increase. The tools provided by the system in support of the tactical decision process are an extremely important addition to the information system. However, of even more importance is the focus brought to strategic issues, such as at what point should a consideration be made to build a new factory or what will be the impact of entering a new market. Strategic issues are discussed in Chapter 10.

STUDY QUESTIONS

1. What is the difference between a tactical decision and a strategic decision?

2. What primary benefits are provided to purchasing through the use of the TOC based manufacturing system?

3. When will purchasing have a conflict with the protection or creation of throughput?

4. Besides the raw material expense, a part's value varies depending on what three internal issues?

5. What minimum information should purchasing have to determine the value of a specific part?

6. When confronted with the possibility that the constraint may run out of material, how much additional expense can the vendor afford to spend to provide the raw material part?

7. What primary issues must be considered when off-loading constraint time to the vendor?

Product	Sales Price	Raw Material	Total CCR Time
A	400	250	30
B	300	100	25
C	100	50	5
D	400	100	45

Figure 9.41 Data for study question 8.

8. From the data in Figure 9.41, determine which products should receive the highest commission schedule per unit and which should receive the least. Explain why.

9. Upon what basis is a decision made to either accept or reject an order?

10. What must be considered when direct labor becomes the constraint and how does this occur?

11. Explain the concept of throughput accounting. How does it differs from cost accounting? Give examples of each.

12. From a quality perspective, what is the most important portion of the net on which to focus to insure the prevention of scrap?

13. Given the data in Figure 9.42, should the decision be to scrap or rework the defective parts? Why?

PRODUCT	CCR TIME/UNIT	CCR TIME AVAIL.
A	15	1500 min
ORDER = 100	SP = $200	RM = $100
DEFECTIVE PARTS	TIME/UNIT	MATERIAL
20	15	$10

Figure 9.42 Data for study question 13.

14. Explain the impact that rework will have on the creation of a schedule. Give examples.

15. What is the formula for computing the effectiveness rating for total productive maintenance (TPM)? List the problems involved with its implementation and give valid solutions for overcoming the problems.

10

Making Strategic Decisions

Strategic decisions by definition will have a major impact on the company. Setting the direction for large portions of the company's assets, they include issues such as what measurement system or systems should be used to focus activity, what strategy to use in entering new markets and when to expand the factory. The decision to use the theory of constraints including the TOC Thinking Process and TOC based information system is definitely a strategic decision. However, for the purposes of this text, strategic decisions will be addressed in the following context:

- Market segmentation
- Company growth
- Long-term planning
- Recession proofing the company

MARKET SEGMENTATION

Entering new markets can be risky for any company. Many who make an attempt lose a great deal of money in the undertaking. If it were not for the entrepreneurial spirit that drives some people to take risks, new ventures would probably be rare. This kind of activity is a natural part of the business world and must continue. So reducing the risk of loss for new ventures while maximizing profit is vitally important.

The objective of market segmentation is to maximize profitability while reducing risk. Managed correctly, the market segmentation strategy can make a big difference in the success rate of new ventures as well as the survival rate of most companies.

There are numerous ways of segmenting the market, for example, by geographical region, by specific product and by customer. However, to be successful certain rules should be followed. As presented by Dr. Goldratt, markets should be segmented so that

- The sales price in one market will not impact the sales price in another.
- The same resource base serves all markets.
- It is unlikely that all segments will be down at the same time.

Companies are not made of numerous resources acting independently, but of throughput chains. As previously defined, a throughput chain is a chain of resources connected by the process of generating throughput. In proper market segmentation, each throughput chain may feed numerous markets so that resources are protected from a downturn in any one market, or in several, so that the company can be more selective in what sales orders it takes. One of the benefits is that the company is able to manipulate the market rather than having the market manipulate the company.

Protecting the Sales Price

If the price of a product being sold into one market is affected by the price in another, the ability to support different pricing structures immediately fails. As an example, a manufacturer of building supplies decides to segment the market based on customer type, one being commercial buildings and the other being residential housing. The same products are sold to both markets. If the product is equally applicable in both environments, the supplier may have great difficulty in offering specific supplies to one builder at one price and to another builder at a different price. However, by modifying each part slightly to change each builder's perception of its usefulness to them, the price requested in one market may have no influence on the other. The benefits can be surprising.

In Figure 10.1, products A and B are made on the same resources and are sold in completely different markets. The price charged for each has no effect on the other. Both markets are fed by the same resources and take the same amount of time to produce. The amount of raw material used to create both is equal so the throughput generated by A is greater by $20. When the constraint is inside the

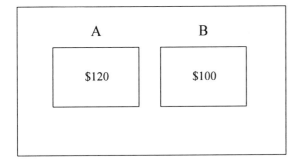

Figure 10.1 Protecting the sales price.

company sales preference is given to A. If for some reason one market becomes soft and the asking price must be lowered to keep business, the price in both markets will not be affected. Profitability may decline, but not as much as it might have.

If a third product, product C, can be made on the same resources to feed a different market segment than products A and B, there may be even more flexibility in price. If there is normally enough volume from markets for A and B to place the constraint in the factory and for some reason market B should become depressed, a third market can be used in conjunction with A and B to continue to fill the factory with work while maintaining price protection in the original markets. When the market for B returns to its normal level, C can be given a lower sales priority depending on the amount of throughput generated per unit of the constraint.

Note: when lowering the price on B or in selling C long-term contracts should be avoided.

Protecting the Resources

If the same manufacturing company had two different sets of resources feeding the commercial and residential markets separately and for some reason one of the markets declines, then those resources which feed the declining market would be threatened. However, if both markets are fed by the same resources and a downturn occurred, then the threat is not as great. Figure 10.2 represents product flow diagrams for products A and B. Each product uses the same resources and must be processed on the constraint; they share the same through-put chain. If demand for either A or B should decline and the markets were perfectly segmented, then resources R-1 through R-3 would not be threatened.

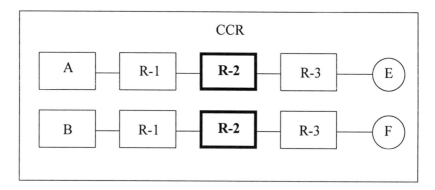

Figure 10.2 Protecting the resources.

Notice that the amount of throughput that can be generated by the throughput chain is limited by resource R-2. If a third market could be found which does not go through R-2, the price flexibility and resource protection would be greatly enhanced. In Figure 10.3 product C represents a third market segmentation.

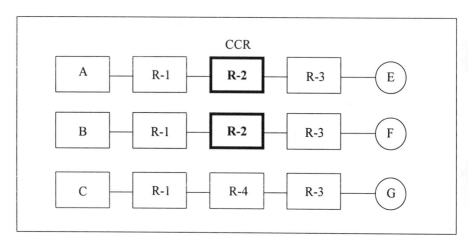

Figure 10.3 Price flexibility and resource protection—adding a third market segment.

Product C uses resources R-1 and R-3, but avoids using resource R-2. In this case price flexibility and resource protection are increased. In addition, if resources R-1, R-3 and R-4 have excess capacity, any price charged for product C over the cost of raw material is all profit. This creates a definite competitive advantage whenever price is a consideration.

However, with the increased utilization of R-1 and R-3 comes the possibility of causing problems for the exploitation of R-2 by interfering with the subordination process of R-1 and R-3. If R-1 and R-3 begin to absorb protective capacity, then the constraint and shipping buffers would need to be enlarged creating an increase in inventory and operating expense. If the additional load caused a secondary constraint, then inventory and operating expense would be increased even more.

The previous example does not mean that when a problem occurs in the subordination process that something is wrong, only that something must be done to protect the constraint under the increased demand. The system will either help in scheduling through the problem or let the user know that schedules must be pushed into the future. If the schedule is pushed and the reason isolated to a specific throughput chain, then increased capacity might be warranted for a specific resource on the chain or the sales department can limit the amount of that particular product being sold. If sales are to be limited, another throughput chain which does not have a limitation should be identified and its excess capacity sold. This process continues until all resource capacity is completely absorbed in the generation of throughput.

Identifying the throughput chains of the company, understanding what their strengths and weaknesses are and then maximizing the market segments fed by each chain will greatly reduce the risk of failure for new market penetration while maximizing the profit generated.

Using the Information System in the Segmentation Strategy

Objectively, having the same resources feed more than one market where the price in one market is not affected by the other is good business. Using the TOC based information system to aid in developing and executing an effective market segmentation strategy can offer a tremendous advantage by helping to

- Generate the strategy
- Identify the strengths and weaknesses of the strategy selected
- Constantly upgrade of the strategy

Generating the Strategy

The key issues in generating the market segmentation strategy include

- Finding the throughput chains
- Assessing the extent of market segmentation for each throughput chain
- Finding and using excess capacity to enhance pricing flexibility and the generation of throughput
- Creating and introducing a new product to further segment the market
- Understanding the impact of additional market segments on the subordination process

The key objective in identifying the throughput chains is to understand which string of resources feed what market segments.

Figure 10.4 is a modification of the descending part/operations screen seen previously. Throughput chain 1 feeds the market with products A, B and C. The string of resources used to accomplish this task include R-1 through R-6. Throughput chain 2 differs from 1 in that it feeds the market with products D, E and F, uses an additional resource (R-7) and does not include resource R-4.

Throughput Chain 1	Throughput Chain 2
PRODUCT A	PRODUCT D
PRODUCT B	PRODUCT E
PRODUCT C	PRODUCT F
R-1	R-1
R-2	R-2
R-3	R-3
R-4	R-5
R-5	R-6
R-6	R-7

Figure 10.4   Identifying the throughput chain.

Notice that the constraint in throughput chain 1 has been placed in bold. Resources which have been designated as primary or secondary constraints should be identified so that resources with excess capacity can be easily found. Notice that throughput chain 2 does not have a resource which has been designated as having a capacity problem.

The market segmentation screen shows each throughput chain and the extent to which it has been segmented (the number of products it feeds). It also shows which string of resources may have additional capacity that can be exploited. Once each chain has been identified, the throughput generated from each product can be compared so that the process of constantly upgrading each market segment can be accomplished. The objective is to continuously look for and identify new products which have increased throughput value.

Figure 10.5 shows the throughput value of each chain. Notice that throughput chain 1 is listed by throughput per unit of the constraint. Since there is no resource limitation in throughput chain 2, it is listed by throughput per unit.

Notice that for throughput chain number 1 the lowest value per unit of the constraint is $7.00. Selling a product below this price would cause a decrease in the amount of throughput generated.

Selling any amounts of D, E and F would be desirable. Since there is no capacity limitation, the value of each product must be judged based on the amount of throughout per unit sold. When the throughput per unit reaches zero, the price of raw material and the sales price are equal and the product should no longer be available.

Throughput Chain 1			Throughput Chain 2		
PROD.	T/uc	Total Throughput	PROD.	Throughput Per Unit	Total Throughput
A	$9.00	$60,000	D	$60.00	$55,000
B	$8.50	$50,000	E	$50.00	$45,000
C	$7.00	$40,000	F	$45.00	$40,000

Figure 10.5 Throughput value of the chain.

When selling excess capacity there are specific rules which apply:

- Do not oversell the market.
- Pick a market which is relatively large so that a small amount of additional product will not upset the current balance and so that it can be entered and exited without major impact.
- Avoid starting a price war.

GROWING THE COMPANY

Understanding how to grow a company based on its strengths is critical from a strategic perspective. It makes no sense to grow based on the weak points within the company. A key issue in the process would obviously be identifying where the weak points are located and how to address them.

Growing the company can mean entering new markets, increasing the size of the current facility, adding resources or hiring new employees. Knowing what the strengths and weaknesses are can help considerably in accomplishing these tasks. It is important to understand that what is being advocated is not avoiding the use of the five-step process of continuous improvement or in using the thinking process to determine what to improve, but recognizing that different throughput chains will be stronger than others when maximizing growth possibilities.

As explained in *The Next Phase of Total Quality Management* a company should build new facilities when every bit of capacity in the old facility is being used to generate throughput and when it is expected that the new resources will have enough segmentation within the market to protect them. If a company wants to grow, it is unwise to do so where price and resource availability are critical.

Building a new facility when there is still available capacity in the old one is wasteful. As seen in market segmentation, the information system can help tremendously in finding and exploiting additional capacity. Simply implementing the five-step process from the perspective of the physical resource which has been identified as the primary constraint ignores the fact that different throughput chains will have different constraints. Most of them will not be physical. They will instead be managerial. Identifying throughput chains where additional capacity is available is an indication that, for those chains, the constraint is not physical. Since every chain must have a constraint, there must be something blocking the creation of additional throughput for that chain other than the physical resource.

Constantly growing the company through the chain which contains the primary constraint will eventually lead to a resource which is very expensive to replace. To continue to grow through this method will require a large outlay of capital. Before making this kind of commitment it would be best to ensure that every other throughput chain is being tapped for as much throughput as possible.

The strongest points within the company and the easiest way to grow is not by constantly focusing on the chain with the primary physical constraint. While it still must be exploited, by nature it is limited in its ability and will cost money to elevate. Most constraints in the company will cost nothing to elevate. Which is preferable?

The most effective directions to grow can be found in the same fashion as discussed for market segmentation. A throughput chain whose resources have no problem in subordinating to the market or constraint schedule and do not create conflicts with other schedules is considered to have excess capacity available. The strongest points will be those throughput chains which do not go through a physical constraint.

In Figure 10.6 the preferred constraint to break is not necessarily R-4. It may be the constraint for throughput chain 2.

Throughput Chain 1	Throughput Chain 2
PRODUCT A	PRODUCT D
PRODUCT B	PRODUCT E
PRODUCT C	PRODUCT F
R-1	R-1
R-2	R-2
R-3	R-3
R-4	R-5
R-5	R-6
R-6	R-7

Figure 10.6 Growing the company.

One method for testing individual strategies would be to simulate the decision after having reviewed each throughput chain to identify how to break its constraint. Key issues include

- The impact of the decision on other throughput chains
- The impact on the primary physical constraint within any throughput chain and where it might go next

Once individual throughput chains have been identified which do not contain resource constraints on the throughput chains list, a final check can be made by attempting to subordinate to the market demand. As an example, a decision is made to increase throughput for throughput chain 2 by adding a new product and market segment. Product H is added and a forecast entered. During the scheduling process a new constraint is created. Fortunately, there are no major conflicts which result in pushing scheduled sales orders into later periods. The impact is registered on the throughput chains list (see Figure 10.7). Notice that resource R-2 has now been identified as a secondary constraint.

While the system has no problem dealing with the schedule for the new product, there may be better choices. The result of creating a market segmentation and selling product H is that protective capacity is used. Lead times as well as inventory and operating expense will increase. If the lead time increases past the

Throughput Chain 1	Throughput Chain 2
PRODUCT A	PRODUCT D
PRODUCT B	PRODUCT E
PRODUCT C	PRODUCT F
	PRODUCT H
R-1	
R-2	R-1
R-3	**R-2**
R-4	R-3
R-5	R-5
R-6	R-6
	R-7

Figure 10.7 Adding products to the throughput chain.

customer's tolerance lead time, new problems could be created. It may be best to first try a segment where a secondary constraint will not be created. However, it may also be possible and just as desirable to do both.

LONG-TERM PLANNING

In long-term planning the objectives are to understand where the company should be one to two years in the future and help guide the process. Understanding the impact that the constraint will have on the company during that period is vital. Key issues include

- Where will the constraint be one to two years from now? How does this compare to where it should be?
- What constraints will be broken along the way and when will they occur?
- What is the advantage of elevating the constraint from one location to the next?
- When the constraint is elevated will the new interaction between resources cause problems in being able to create a schedule?
- What would be the impact of building a new facility?
- If a decline in market price for a specific product is expected to continue, at what point should the product be dropped from the catalog?

The information system can help in the process by comparing different strategies for elevation over long periods. It can also help determine at what point a new resource should be purchased and what the impact to the decision process will be if it is done.

Elevating the Constraint

Once the constraint has been elevated the impact can be quite extensive. notice the difference between Figures 10.8 and 10.9. If resource R-4 is the constraint, product A is the most profitable and product D the least. If resource R-6 is the constraint, however, product D is the most profitable and product C the least. This change in the location of the constraint causes a major shift in how the company operates, how much money it is generating, and where to focus improvements. The TOC based information system can be used as a simulation tool to determine the impact of changes that may occur months into the future, thereby providing management with the ability to see the impact of the strategic decisions.

Resource R-4

Product	Sales Price	Raw Material	Throughput Generated	Total CCR Time	T/uc
A	300	150	150	15	$10.00
B	310	150	160	20	$8.00
C	200	100	100	15	$6.67
D	400	150	250	45	$5.56

Figure 10.8   Elevating the constraint example—resource R-4 is the constraint.

It is important to understand that the information system assumes no policy constraints. It only deals in the physical interfaces of resources as they are impacted by the environment in which they exist. If a physical constraint is

Resource R-6

Product	Sales Price	Raw Material	Throughput Generated	Total CCR Time	T/uc
D	400	150	250	20	$12.50
B	310	150	160	15	$10.67
A	300	150	150	20	$7.50
C	200	100	100	30	$3.33

Figure 10.9   Elevating the constraint—resource R-6 is the constraint.

preventing the increase of throughput, the system can deal with it. If a policy constraint exists, the system can only reflect the impact that the policy is having on the physical resources. In the long-term planning process, policy constraints are just as active as physical ones. The system assumes that they will be solved.

RECESSION PROOFING

Recession proofing occurs when the company

- Continuously implements the five steps
- Minimizes the impact of a downturn in the economy by protecting resources through market segmentation
- Uses a valid decision process

The information system can help by

- Providing the basis for a valid decision process
- Managing the physical resources and scheduling the factory
- Providing a focal point for implementing the five steps
- Aiding in the identification and elimination of policy constraints
- Setting the proper resource strategy for maximizing the creation of throughput while minimizing the risk

SUMMARY

More than just a replacement for the cost accounting system, the TOC based information system can offer a tremendous advantage in the strategic planning at the corporate level. It is a strategic weapon which can be used to support and guide the future growth and direction of the manufacturing company and is currently being used in numerous companies around the country

STUDY QUESTIONS

1. Explain the concept of marketing segmentation and list the three primary rules.

2. What advantages does proper marketing segmentation provide?

3. List at least four methods of segmenting the market.

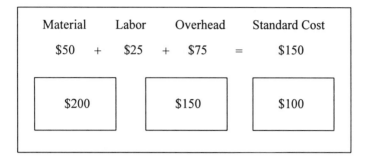

Material		Labor		Overhead		Standard Cost
$50	+	$25	+	$75	=	$150

$200	$150	$100

Figure 10.10   Data for study question 4.

4. Given the information in Figure 10.10, what is the profit margin for the $200, $150 and $100 market segments? Assume excess capacity.

5. What key issues are involved in the generation of the market segmentation strategy and what can the TOC based manufacturing system do to help?

6. Explain the advantage of using excess capacity as a weapon in the process of growing the company. What are its pitfalls?

7. Using the manufacturing system, how is excess capacity identified?

8. Eliminating regulatory issues, at what point should a company consider building a new plant?

11

Modifying the Current System

Although the tendency at this point might be to throw out the traditional system and start over, this is not a good answer to the problem of making the transition to the new system. More to the point, the issue should be what processes and file structures should be kept, added, or eliminated. Understanding this is critical to the process of migration toward the TOC based system.

As explained earlier, the new system is quite different from the old in a number of ways. Gone are the technologies of MRP, CRP and the traditional shop floor scheduling methods for certain resources. Also missing is cost accounting and accounting methods such as labor and overhead allocation to work orders. Added are those processes and tools that support the five steps of improvement and throughput decision-making.

The traditional MRP based system provides a tremendous platform on which to build. Chapter 11 will be a presentation of the end product and will describe the contents of an information system designed for the manufacturing environment.

CHAPTER OBJECTIVES

- To present a detailed model of the new information system
- To define what must be done to modify the traditional system
- To define the interfaces required

As seen earlier, the TOC based information system (see Figure 11.1):

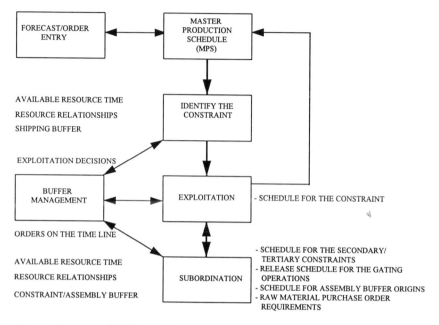

Figure 11.1 The TOC based system.

- Relies on the output of the master production schedule
- Identifies the constraint by comparing those resources which have taken the most protective or productive capacity from the system
- Exploits the constraint by building a schedule and maximizing its effectiveness through setup savings, overtime or offloading
- Subordinates the remaining resources to the schedule produced during the exploitation phase
- Buffers the system from those things which can and will go wrong and is used to focus on improvements, establish lead times and determine the release schedule for raw material

These processes will require that certain data be maintained and used as input. Purchase orders and sales orders must be written, part numbers and inventory need to be maintained, money must be received, and employees as well as vendors and the government must be paid. The traditional system has made great progress in supporting these areas. A very large portion of the system needs no modification at all.

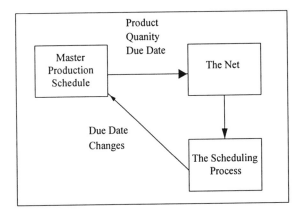

Figure 11.2 Linking the master production schedule.

UNDERSTANDING WHERE CHANGE WILL OCCUR

Master Production Scheduling

The traditional master production scheduling procedure will probably remain as the origination of input and definition of demand for the system. Little, if any, modification is required other than creating a link between the schedule for the constraint, the MPS file and the net (see Figure 11.2).

It is the master production schedule which actually helps foster the generation of the net. After the master schedule has been set, demand is then passed from the MPS in the form of sales order/product numbers, including quantity and due dates, to the program designed to create the net. It is the MPS that determines the part/operations required to produce to the demand of the sales orders and the forecast (see Figure 11.3). As will be seen, the MPS does not provide the only data that need to be passed to the net generation program.

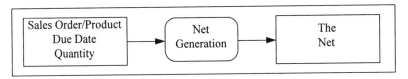

Figure 11.3 Linking the MPS.

Note: the sales order/product number is similar to the part/operation in that one string of characters is used to identify the product ordered by the customer and the sales order number.

Linking to the Constraint

The link between the schedule of the primary constraint and the master production schedule is made so that the MPS will accurately reflect the due date of the sales order or forecast. When changes occur as a result of the scheduling process the new dates are passed to the MPS file.

To update sales order and forecast due dates, the completion date and time from the constraint schedule is used. During the scheduling process the system will push those orders into the future which have rod or buffer violations. These changes are made by adding the length of the shipping buffer to the date the order is to be completed on the primary constraint (see Figure 11.4).

Part/operation B/30 was originally scheduled to cross the primary constraint (R-4) by hour 8:00 on day 99. The sales order was schedule to be shipped 8 hours later according to the shipping buffer. Part/operation B/30 has been rescheduled to day 100 hour 4:30. Notice that S/O111's due date and time have also been pushed into the future by the length of the shipping buffer.

Figure 11.4 Pushing the order.

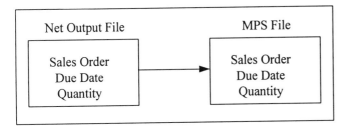

Figure 11.5 The link between the MPS and the net.

Note: if a secondary constraint has been created between the primary constraint and the sales order, then the sales order due date will be modified based on the date the order is to be completed on the secondary constraint.

To accomplish this task there must be a link created between the sales order due date from the output of the scheduling process and the master schedule (see Figure 11.5).

Since the output of the net feeds directly to the MPS file, the traditional available and available to promise (ATP) data should be readily accessible (see Figure 11.6).

Checking Finished Goods Inventory

Since the net actually starts with the sales order/product number and the TOC scheduling process is capable of checking inventory on hand as well as demand

Figure 11.6 Available to promise schedule.

for end items required by the sales order or the forecast, there is no need to offset sales order demand for on-hand inventory prior to placing demand data into the net.

Note: as presented in Chapter 2, rough-cut capacity planning (RCCP) will be eliminated and completely replaced by the TOC scheduling process.

Material and Capacity Planning

Other features of the traditional system that are to be eliminated and replaced by the TOC scheduling process include gross-to-net requirements generation (MRP) and capacity requirements planning (CRP). As the TOC scheduling process creates a schedule for the buffer origins and diverging operations, it is also generating the release schedule to gating operations and order information for raw material. To do this the system must know what material has already been produced, what is left to produce, and the individual timing of orders. As seen in earlier chapters, the planning of material and capacity requirements is actually imbedded in the TOC logic for identification, exploitation and subordination.

Action Messages

Action message processing, a standard feature in most traditional systems, can be maintained for managing purchased parts and for designating the release schedule at gating operations. Action messages include

- Order launch
- Defer
- Cancel
- Expedite

To obtain an action message the output of the TOC scheduling process should be connected to the facility used to present the message. Obviously, before the system will know what orders to defer or expedite the purchase order identity must be matched to the demand of the schedule.

Shop Floor Reporting

To aid in the scheduling and decision-making processes, the location of work in process (WIP) inventory must be known. Orders must be tracked and information fed back to the net and to buffer management so that they can work with current data. The traditional method for tracking orders at specific operations by logging in or out can still be used. Emphasis should be placed on what part/operations have been completed and where the work in process inventory is.

Rather than reporting every part/operation at every resource, it may be beneficial to report one part/operation and have a number of them automatically updated. The act of reporting milestones for part/operations other than those for which a schedule has been created can still be useful.

Labor Collection

Labor collection, a part of the traditional shop floor system used to feed cost accounting, can under normal circumstances be eliminated. Since these data will no longer be used in the decision process, hourly employees will only need to record the time they are at work for pay purposes.

Dispatching

A method of determining the sequencing, start times and stop times at locations such as the constraint(s) will still be necessary. The traditional dispatch report used to sequence orders at specific locations on the shop floor (see Figure 11.7)

	Dispatch Report R-4				
Order No.	Part/oper.	Qty	Day	Start	Finish
W/O111	A/20	50	100	00:00	01:00
W/O222	D/20	30	100	01:01	01:45
W/O123	G/30	75	100	01:46	03:46
W/O333	B/10	10	100	03:47	05:00
W/O124	A/20	30	100	05:01	06:30
W/O167	A/20	40	100	06:31	07:45

Figure 11.7 Dispatching schedule.

is to be replaced by the constraint or assembly schedules (see Figure 11.21). The schedule maintained for each operation can be eliminated for all but the buffer origins and diverging operations. The method of relating order sequencing will be by start date/time and finish date/time only. Sequencing methods such as slack time per operation and next queue should not be used.

A majority of resources will be sequenced based on the timing of material released at gating operations. Actual sequencing for those operations will be first come, first serve. When an order is received it should begin processing immediately and be completed as fast as possible.

Note: the objective of the non-constraint schedule (see Figure 11.22) is slightly different. It is used to tell the operator not to start an order before a specified date and time.

Shop Paper

The paperwork necessary to process an order will be very similar to what is currently distributed with the traditional system. It should include

- A list of the parts needed for processing
- The routing
- Any special processing instructions needed at the work station

Depending on the environment, product flow should be fairly easy to distinguish. Routings as well as parts lists may be unnecessary. However, the shop packet should include some way of distinguishing what product is being produced and what sales order or orders are to be filled.

Buffer Management

Buffer management will become an important part of shop floor control. A method of presenting the zones and health statistics of the buffer with current orders would be very helpful. In addition, statistics should be maintained on the buffer management worksheets and periodically consolidated into reports. There are benefits to having each of these features accessible from an interactive screen and on reports. Both should be available. Figure 11.8 is a screen presentation of the buffer in front of the constraint. The information to the right provides the health indicators for zones I and II of the buffer and details about the current order being processed.

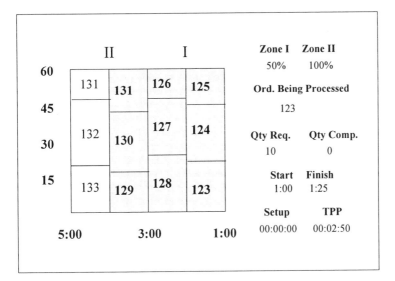

Figure 11.8   The buffer management screen.

Note: zone III and the area used to depict orders which have arrived too early are not shown due to a lack of space (see Chapter 8).

In the box to the left is a graphical representation of the orders which are supposed to be in the buffer along with the specific order numbers. Notice that all of zone I is full while 50% of zone II is full. Each column represents one hour. Notice also from the number of columns that are full that there are three hours of work in front of the constraint. Order 123 is just getting started. Current time is 1:00.

The system should support the ability to display detail information about any order in the buffer. For those orders which have not reached the buffer but should be in zone I or II, the current location should be shown so that the order can be found and either tracked or expedited.

Figure 11.9 is the same detailed information as in Figure 11.8. The additional data in the box belong to order 124. The part sitting in the constraint buffer is station A/30 for sales order S/OABC. There are a quantity of 10, which take 2.5 minutes each to process.

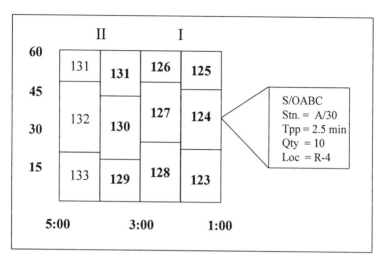

Figure 11.9 The buffer management screen—order detail.

Accounting

The traditional practice of allocating labor and overhead for the purposes of making decisions should be eliminated from the system. However, there will still be financial indicators. Specific data used in the TOC decision process must be made available and includes

- Raw material cost
- Sales price
- Operating expense
- Inventory value
- The accumulated value of throughput dollar days
- The accumulated value of inventory dollar days

With the exception of throughput and inventory dollar days, the traditional system is quite capable of maintaining data on all of the above. Most accounting systems are equipped with the ability to re-organize the chart of accounts for reporting purposes and can present reports showing the current and past period's throughput, inventory and operating expense figures.

By eliminating the labor and overhead values in the item cost records and leaving only inventory cost, the gross margin (the difference between sales price and the cost of goods sold) becomes the throughput figure. By using the output

NET PROFIT = THROUGHPUT – OPERATING EXPENSE

RETURN ON INVESTMENT = $\dfrac{\text{THROUGHPUT} - \text{OPERATING EXPENSE}}{\text{INVENTORY}}$

Figure 11.10 Calculating net profit and return on investment measurements.

of the scheduling process to predict the orders being sold and subtracting the raw material cost, a projection can be made of the future throughput to be generated by the company. Combined with operating expense and inventory projections, familiar financial measurements can be determined for future as well as current and past periods. Figure 11.10 presents the formulas for computing net profit and return on investment from these data. Figure 11.11 presents productivity and inventory turns measurements.

Note: these measurements were initially presented by Dr. Goldratt in *The Haystack Syndrome.*

Some companies will want to use the total variable cost method. The total variable cost of an order is determined by adding those costs which can be directly attributable to a given order, such as commissions and landed costs. Landed costs are those costs associated with transportation, taxes and duties and are generally added to the cost of raw material. The result is then subtracted from the sales price to determine throughput.

PRODUCTIVITY = $\dfrac{\text{THROUGHPUT}}{\text{OPERATING EXPENSE}}$

INVENTORY TURNS = $\dfrac{\text{THROUGHPUT}}{\text{INVENTORY}}$

Figure 11.11 Calculating productivity and inventory turns measurements.

Purchasing

The purchasing system will require no changes. The traditional system works fine for organizing, placing and tracking orders with vendors. However, there are some other issues which need to be addressed.

Purchasing receives from the scheduling system a list of parts, quantities and due dates. Prior to creating any action messages for placing an order, a comparison must be made with the current on order data. At that time notices can be generated which will request that purchase orders be created, deferred, expedited or canceled.

Additionally, as discussed earlier, purchasing needs access to the scheduling/decision system to understand the importance of certain parts when decisions need to be made, such as whether or not to pay a premium to get a part flown in or whether to purchase a part that is currently made internally.

INTEGRATING WITH THE CURRENT SYSTEM

As earlier defined, the base for the scheduling portion of the new system is the net. It provides in one file a model of how individual resources are connected, including

- All open orders and forecasted items with the product name or number, the amount of demand for each and the due date
- A list of all part/operations and how they are sequenced, including the time per part (run time and setup), the amount of inventory completed at each part/operation and the resource on which they are processed
- A list of all resources and the quantity available
- All raw material, including the quantity on hand and lead time

Additional information used in the scheduling process includes the individual buffer sizes for constraint, shipping and assembly buffers as well as a shop calendar with the work day hours and overtime availability.

Except for the buffer data and possibly allowable overtime, all the data provided to create the net currently exist in various files within the traditional system:

- All open orders and forecasts originate from the master production schedule.
- Resource information is obviously found in the resource file.
- The part/operation is a combination of the bills of material and route files.
- Raw material and the quantity on hand can be found in the inventory or item master files.

The benefit to placing all these data in one file is processing speed. For an information system to be effective it must provide immediate feedback. To answer a simple question such as what lot size to use should not take hours, only minutes or perhaps seconds. With all scheduling information stored in one file and placed in CPU memory, all disk access can be virtually eliminated from the process.

Input to the Net

Figure 11.12 illustrates the transfer of data—including the bills of material, routings, raw material inventory, resource data and work in process inventory— from the traditional system to the net. Data elements from each of these files are transferred to the net to facilitate the implementation of the five steps.

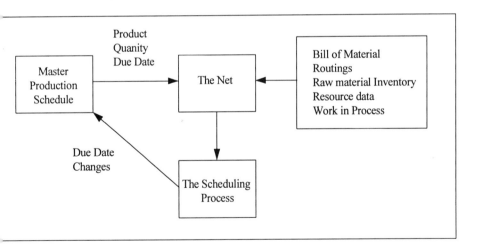

Figure 11.12 The TOC based system.

Master	Raw	Resource	Part/	Order of
Schedule	Material	Data	Operation	Processing
S/O/prod.	RM Part	Resource	Part/op.	To part/op.
Quantity	Stock qty.	Quantity	Resource	From part/op.
Due date	Lead time		Run time	Quantity
			Setup time	Scrap
			Alt. resource	Rework
			Run time	Rework part/op.
			Setup time	
			Inventory (WIP)	

Figure 11.13   Input to the net.

Generating the Net

The net is generated by taking specific data from each of the sources listed in Figure 11.13 and placing them into one file. The data that originated on the traditional system is used as input to the TOC based system.

Notice that the input data has been split into five different categories. Each category contains the specifics required to generate the net. In addition to the master schedule detail already discussed, the data categories include

- Raw material
- Resource data
- Part/operations
- Order of processing (to/from)

Raw Material Data

Raw material includes the raw material part number required to build the demand generated by the master schedule, the quantity currently in stock and the lead time required to replenish stock (see Figure 11.14).

Resource Data

Resource data includes the resource identity of those resources used in the current production plan and the quantity or number of resources available (see Figure 11.15).

Raw Material Data		
Raw Material	Stock Amount	Lead Time
A	10	10
B	50	25
C	30	20
D	20	10
E	110	30

Figure 11.14 Raw material data.

Part/Operation Data

Part/operation data include the part/operation to be produced, the resource where production is to occur, and the run and setup times used to produce the part at that resource (see Figure 11.16).

Resource Data	
Resource	Quantity
R-1	1
R-2	2
R-3	2
R-4	1
R-5	2
R-6	3
R-7	1
R-8	1

Figure 11.15 Resource data.

Part/Op	Resource	Run Time	Setup Time	Alt. Res.	Run Time	Setup Time
1234/10	R-7	1.0	1.0	R-8	1.3	1.0
1234/20	R-5	1.5	1.5	R-2	2.0	1.5
1234/30	R-4	1.0	1.0	R-6	1.5	1.0

Figure 11.16   Part/operation data.

Order of Processing Data

The order of processing (to/from) category designates the order in which processing is to occur. The "to part/operation" is the recipient of a completed "from part/operation." The quantity indicates the bill of material relationship. In other words, in order to build a to part/operation it will take a specific number of from part/operations. In addition, a to part/operation may have more than one from part/operation reporting to it, just as in a bill of material. The from part/operation which has more than one part/operation reporting to it is called an assembly, or converging operation. "Scrap" is the percentage figure used to increase the number of from part/operations required to produce the to part/operation based on the amount of scrap that may occur at the from part/operation. "Rework" is the percentage of rework expected, while "rework part/operation" indicates where the rework is to take place. In Figure 11.17,

Order of Processing					
To Part/Op	From Part/Op	Quantity	Scrap	Rework	Rework Part/Op
Ord1/F	1234/30	1	.05	.10	1234/10
1234/30	1234/20	1	.05	.10	1234/30
1234/20	1234/10	1	.05	.10	1234/20
1234/10	A	1	.10	.10	1234/10
1234/10	B	3	.10	.10	1234/10
1234/10	C	1	.00	.10	1234/10
1234/10	D	1	.00	.10	1234/10
1234/10	E	1	.00	.10	1234/10

Figure 11.17   Order of processing.

part/operation 1234/10 must receive raw materials A, B, C, D and E. There is a bill of material relationship between raw material B and part/operation 1234/10 of 3 to 1. If part/operation 1234/10 is to be reworked, it will be performed at part/operation 1234/10.

Part/operation 1234/10 feeds part/operation 1234/20, which in turn feeds part/operation 1234/30. Once part/operation 1234/30 is used to fill each requirement of product F on sales order Ord1.

For each 1234/30 that's processed, 5% are expected to be scrapped and 10% are expected to be reworked. The rework is to take place at part/operation 1234/30. The part/operation detail (Figure 11.16) indicates that part/operation 1234/30 is to be processed on resource R-4.

Note: order of processing in this case does not refer to the order of processing on the net discussed in Chapter 7.

The Origination of Data for the Net

The data used to create the net originate from the traditional system. Figure 11.18 indicates specifically from where. Notice that all the data for the master schedule and resource categories originate from either the master schedule or resource files. Raw material data are taken from the item master and inventory files, while part/operation and order of processing data originate in the bill of material and route files.

Note: obviously, each MRP system is designed differently and, as such, may have different file structures. Data storage such as inventory may be placed in a

Master Schedule	Raw Material	Resource Data	Part/ Operation	Order of Processing
Master Schedule	Item Master	Resource	Bill of Material	Bill of Material
	Inventory		Routing	Routing

Figure 11.18 The origination of data for the net.

file which manages all inventory-related data such as on hand and on order. The objective of this section is to present basic relationships between the data on the traditional system and the input requirements to the net, not to present a solution for a specific application.

In addition to the data already mentioned, the TOC based system requires

- A horizon length to understand what orders to load onto the time line (Note: it may not be necessary to load all orders to make a decision.)
- The buffer lengths for each buffer type, including shipping, constraint and assembly to protect the weak points within the system
- The maximum overtime that can be applied per day or week during the auto- overtime function
- The amount of artificial load, in percentage terms, to automatically add to resources which are scheduled to maximum capacity for a set number of consecutive days
- A shop day calendar indicating the work hours per day and the work days available during the year

These data are actually stored outside the traditional system files but are used by the net.

Output of the Net

The output of the net can be found in Figure 11.19. Notice that the output includes the schedule for each buffer origin, the release schedule to the gating operations, a schedule for those resources which occur immediately following the diverging operations, the raw material requirements for purchasing, and the overtime requirements for production.

Note: the schedule for resources which process parts immediately following a diverging operation are scheduled to insure that part/operations are not processed before a specific time and are processed in only a specific amount, nothing more.

Figure 11.20 is a detailed list of those data provided after all three steps (identification, exploitation and subordination) of the scheduling process have been completed.

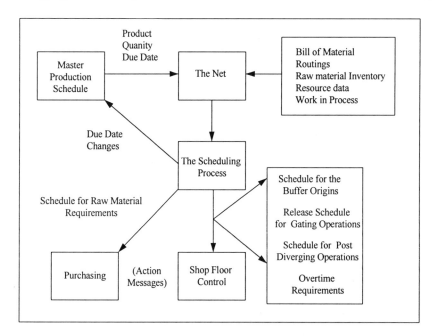

Figure 11.19 The information system.

Constraint(s) Schedule	Non-Constraint Schedule	Release Schedule	Raw Mat. Schedule	Sales Order Schedule	Overtime Schedule
Constraint ID	Resource ID	Resource ID	RM Part	Sales Order	Resource
Order ID	Order ID	Part/Op	Stock Qty	Due Date	Date
Part/Op	Start Date/Time	Quantity	Order Date	Quantity	Amount
Order/Prod	Due Date/Time	Start Date/Time	Delivery Date		
Quantity			Order Number		
Run Time					
Setup Time					
Start Date/Time					
Finish Date/Time					
Orig. Date/Time					

Figure 11.20 Output from the scheduling process.

Constraint(s) Schedule

Constraint ID	Order ID	Part/Op	Order/Prod	Qty	Run Time	Setup Time	Start Date/ Time	Finish Date/ Time	Orig Date/ Time
R-4	1234	A/30	S/O111/X	50	50.:00	1:00	100/1:00	106/4:00	106/8:00
R-4	1235	H/30	S/O333/Y	20	20.:00	1:50	106/4:01	108/5:50	108/8:00
R-4	1236	G/30	S/O222/Z	30	30.:00	2:00	108/5:51	112/5:51	113/8:00
R-4	1238	N/20	S/O111/Q	60	30.:00	1:00	112/5:52	116/4:52	116/8:00
R-4	1239	F/30	S/O444/R	10	20.:00	1:50	116/4:53	119/0:50	118/8:00

Figure 11.21   The constraint schedule.

The Constraint Schedule

Output from the constraint(s) schedule includes the identification of the constraint resources, the identification of the orders which must cross it, the order/product involved, the quantity of each, the run time, the setup time, the start date and completion date of each order, and the original completion date and time (see Figure 11.21).

Note: order ID refers to an internal designation for the identification of a specific part operation on the constraint schedule.

The Non-Constraint Schedule

The non-constraint schedule represents, in detail, a schedule used to prevent certain action from taking place before a specific time (see Figure 11.22).

Res. ID	Order ID	Start Date/ Time	Due Date/ Time
R-1	Ord/123	106/4:30	107/3:30
R-1	Ord/234	108/2:30	109/3:30
R-1	Ord/245	110/4:30	111/2:30
R-1	Ord/234	116/2:30	116/7:30

Figure 11.22   The non-constraint schedule.

Notice that the start and stop times for each order are not consecutive. In other words, when order Ord/123 is complete at day 107 hour 3:30, order Ord/234 does not begin immediately. In fact, it does not start until almost one day later. This does not mean that resource R-1 does not have any work other than what is shown on the schedule. It only means that for some reason the system does not want these orders to begin before a specified date and time. The reason may be that resource R-1 has inventory that it could process, but because this inventory is to be used at another resource, R-1 is told not to process until a specific time. By processing the inventory before the designated time, R-1 could be taking material which was intended for other purposes.

The Release Schedule

Another output of the system is the release schedule for the gating operations. In Figure 11.23, R-7 is to begin processing part/operation 123/10 for a quantity of 100 at day 100, hour 3:30. This tells production control when to release the order and when the raw material should be presented to the resource R-7 to begin production. Part/operation 234/10 is to be released a day later at hour 2:30.

In addition to understanding when to begin processing a specific part/operation, it is also important to understand what raw material will be required to begin the process. The order of processing data within the net should indicate this (see Figure 11.24).

Release Schedule

Res. ID	Part/Op.	Qty	Start Date/ Time
R-7	123/10	100	100/3:30
R-7	234/10	150	101/2:30
R-8	245/10	200	101/2:30
R-8	234/10	100	101/7:30

Figure 11.23 The release schedule.

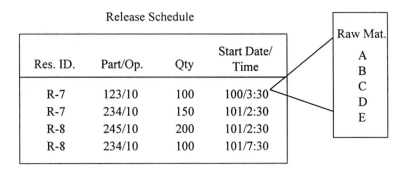

Release Schedule

Res. ID.	Part/Op.	Qty	Start Date/ Time	Raw Mat.
R-7	123/10	100	100/3:30	A B C D E
R-7	234/10	150	101/2:30	
R-8	245/10	200	101/2:30	
R-8	234/10	100	101/7:30	

Figure 11.24   The release schedule showing ram material detail information.

The Raw Material Schedule

The raw material schedule indicates what raw material needs to be purchased, when the order should be placed and when to schedule delivery. In addition, it makes a direct connection to the sales order involved. (see Figure 11.25).

Sales Orders Schedule

The sales order schedule indicates the specific sales order, when it is due and the quantity to be shipped (see Figure 11.26). Also included is an indication of whether the order is late or on time based on the extent of penetration into the buffer. Notice that sales order S/O333 for product Y at a quantity of 15 is due on shop day 90. It is also indicating that because S/O333 has penetrated over 50% of the shipping buffer it will be late.

RM Part	Order Qty	Order Date	Delivery Date	Sales Order
Gasket	100	100	107	S/O111/X
Bolt	150	101	107	S/O333/Y
Battery	200	101	107	S/O222/Z
Pipe	100	101	108	S/O222/Z

Figure 11.25   Raw material schedule.

Order/ Prod	Qty	Due Date	Past Due
S/O111/X	10	90	N
S/O333/Y	15	91	Y
S/O222/Z	20	91	N
S/O222/Z	10	91	N

Figure 11.26 Sales order schedule.

Overtime Requirements Schedule

When generating the schedule, a decision must be made whether or not to use the manual or auto-overtime features discussed earlier. If the feature is used and overtime is added, what resource or resources will receive the overtime and when? The overtime requirements schedule is designed to answer these questions. It lists the resource on which the overtime is to be performed, the date and the amount of overtime required by the schedule (see Figure 11.27).

Resource R-4 has been scheduled overtime on shop days 97, 98, 101 and 102. The amount of time required by the schedule is 2 hours, 1 hour and 50 minutes, 2 hours and 1 hour, respectively. These data can be readily used to compute the increase in operating expense necessary to support the schedule as well as plan labor requirements during the schedule horizon.

Resource	Date	Amount
R-4	97	2:00
R-4	98	1:50
R-4	101	2:00
R-4	102	1:00

Figure 11.27 The overtime requirements schedule.

Software Development

Integration and implementation of any information system will require the creation of at least four environments within the computer:

- Development
- Testing
- Conference room pilot
- Production

Modifying the traditional system should be no different. The objective is to protect each environment so that as the project progresses it can be controlled. Programs which have been developed by the programming staff should not be placed directly into production without being tested first. Individual programs and modules are tested by applications specialists in the testing environment once programming is complete. If a problem occurs, the programmer is notified and the problem resolved.

While the system is being developed and tested, procedures are written to explain to the end user how the system is to operate. The conference room pilot is used to test the system and the written procedures in their entirety once the integration process is complete. Upon completion, the software with all tested modifications is placed into production. Production is where the actual end user of the system becomes involved.

There is currently a fledgling industry of small software development companies which have TOC based software that can be readily integrated into most standard MRPII type systems. This will help considerably in the process and, since the preferred method of structuring the system may be client/server, the PC based system may be the best route to take.

If for some reason the size of the company prevents the use of a PC based scheduling system (industries such as aircraft manufacturing will have part/operations in the millions), then the more traditional integration process may be necessary. However, starting from scratch without the benefit of experience in the development of TOC based software could be a nightmare. It may be best to take an existing system and port it to another platform.

The Platform

There are two issues as to where the files and logic of the system should be placed to maximize its effectiveness given the current computer technology:

- If the logic is to be placed on the host then it must be capable of processing multiple schedules simultaneously as people are attempting to make decisions. This could seriously disrupt the response time for other tasks which must be performed.
- If it is to be placed on the personal computer, then everyone would be able to process their decisions independently without impacting the response time. However, if the files and schedules involved in the decision process are not duplicated on each machine, then each person may approach the decision process differently.

As an example, production control sets a schedule for the factory and engineering must make a decision on how money is to be spent for improvements. Engineering then creates a separate schedule. During the process, engineering makes different decisions while exploiting the constraint and performing subordination, or they start the process with different data residing in the net. The resulting decision may be different than what is actually required. Engineering may use money to fix the wrong resource. Unless the factory and the decision process are in sync the decision process will be constantly variable and will not be based on the reality which currently exists on the shop floor.

It may be that the best environment for this technology is client/server. There are some very convincing arguments for this position.

- If the net were to exist and be maintained on a server, as changes happen within the factory a data repository would exist which would be consistent for everyone without placing the burden on the host.
- If the logic for scheduling, subordination and buffer management were on the server as well, then any time a need arises to have one primary schedule it could be easily done.
- If the logic were to be duplicated on the client and an ability existed to pull the net from the server into CPU memory on the client, then independent decisions could be supported without placing the burden on the server.

Figure 11.28 provides an illustration of the client/server organization of the system. The host would maintain the data repository for primary file maintenance including sales orders, purchase orders and the item master. The server would maintain:

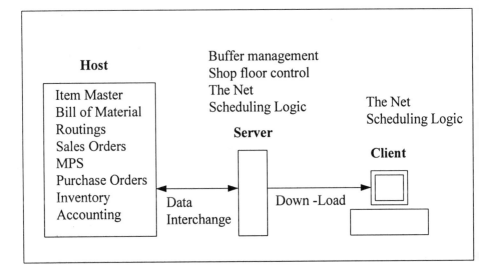

Figure 11.28   The client/server environment.

- The buffer management system
- Shop floor control
- The net
- Scheduling logic

The data necessary to maintain the net on the server or the data files on the host can be downloaded and uploaded at specific intervals during the day. The client would maintain a copy of the logic necessary to support the decision process. Any time a decision is to be made at any level in the company a current copy of the net can be pulled into the client for processing.

An alternative to this configuration would be to go directly to the host, download the requisite files and generate the net at the PC level for each department. To prevent accidental modifications of the primary net, separate files can be maintained for different simulations as well as the primary schedule (see Figure 11.29).

The advantages to using client/server are

- The host is free to maintain communication to all users for maintaining data without being burdened by the scheduling or decision processes.

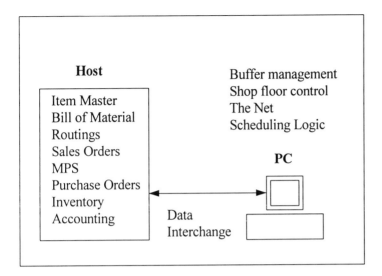

Figure 11.29 Interfacing directly to the PC.

- The scheduling process can be performed at any time.
- Users can make decisions any time.

SUMMARY

The nature of the information system continues to improve as more and more companies adopt the theory of constraints. It is important for current information systems developers to understand where the traditional system should be modified and how it can be accomplished.

STUDY QUESTIONS

1. In the transition from the MRP based system to the TOC based system, what features will more than likely be eliminated and what features kept?

2. What data are required to build the net and from where will it originate on the traditional system?

3. What are the minimum four stages of software development or integration that should be used during the technical phase of the implementation?

4. What steps within the five-step process will contain at least a portion of the logic used to plan material requirements?

5. What steps within the five-step process will contain at least a portion of the logic used to generate the schedule?

6. What portion of the system will be used to replace capacity requirements planning?

7. Present at least three examples of how the system will be used to replace cost accounting. Include a decision model in the examples.

8. Explain the concept of total variable cost and how it should be used in the system to make decisions.

9. Explain in detail the physical laws which are involved in the creation of the dynamic buffering process. (Research question.)

10. What is the objective of the order of processing category of data taken from the MRP data files?

11. What is the objective of the non-constraint schedule?

12. What data input requirements are needed to feed back to the system through shop floor control?

13. What part/operation data are required to generate the schedule and where does it originate on the host manufacturing system?

14. What data are required to build the schedule, but are not located on the host manufacturing system?

15. What data are contained in the following schedules and what are they used for?

    • The release schedule
    • The raw material schedule
    • The sales order schedule
    • The overtime requirements schedule

12

Implementation

Implementing a different kind of system will mean using a different approach. This chapter presents the basic structure of how a TOC based information system should be implemented. The key issue is to ensure that when the implementation is complete, the company will be able to use the system to attain its goal. This means that not only should the system be available and working properly, but also that it should be used to support the implementation of the theory of constraints.

CHAPTER OBJECTIVES

- To present a method of implementation for the TOC based information system
- To discuss the obstacles which may block a successful implementation and how to deal with them

DEFINING A SUCCESSFUL IMPLEMENTATION

Implementing a TOC based system represents is a change from the traditional approach for a number of reasons:

- The logic of the system is very different and will require a total change in how the planning process is executed.

- It means implementing the theory of constraints at the same time. This alone is a monumental task.
- It requires a change in how the factory is organized, from either a work order, rate based or just-in-time environment to the drum-buffer-rope process.
- It changes drastically the role of the information system in the decision process.

The objective of the implementation of a TOC based information system is to provide a tool to be used by the company in reaching its goal.

The implementation will be successful when those who must use the system in the implementation of the five steps can do so with predictable results, and when the results are in line with the goal of the corporation.

Predictable results can be obtained when

- A road map exists which defines the goal of the company and how to get there
- A reliable process exists in a stable environment which will give the same results under the same conditions every time
- A method exists to quantify the result of a specific action or provide evidence that a specific action will produce a quantifiable result
- The process is not blocked during execution.

THE IMPLEMENTATION PROCESS

Since each implementation involves more than simply providing a scheduling platform, the discussion has been split into three parts with each topic having significant importance:

1. The technical implementation
2. The physical implementation
3. The logical implementation

The Technical Implementation

The technical implementation involves preparing the system so that it can perform the scheduling function. It includes:

- Selecting the platform
- Creating the interface
- Preparing the net
- Security
- Testing the logic

For our purposes, we will assume that a traditional manufacturing system currently exists and that the data management processes—such as part master data and bills of material management, sales order processing, purchasing and inventory management, etc.—have been implemented and that they are functioning correctly.

Selecting the platform

Obviously, the selection of the platform on which the system is to be run cannot be determined without understanding some key issues relating to the vendor or designer for the specific application. However, there are some guidelines which can be used to ensure maximum performance from the users perspective. Key issues include

- Central processing unit (CPU) speed
- The amount of internal (CPU) memory
- Disk space

If the objective is to use the system to make decisions, then the speed at which data is manipulated must be such that any decision can be made in less than 10–15 minutes. That is the purpose of shrinking the total size of the data to be manipulated to the size of one file and placing it in internal memory. By limiting the amount of disk access requirements, the TOC based system takes advantage of the advances being made in computer processor speeds. Using internal memory can increase the rate at which data are manipulated 10–20,000 times and, according to IBM, the increase in processing speeds will climb exponentially over the next few years.

While the speed at which the data is manipulated is a function of the processor used, the size of the internal memory is directly related to the size of the net. In configuring the system, it is important to know the maximum amount of data that will be stored in memory without having to go to the disk. Since the net is comprised of part/operations, there will be a direct correlation between the number of part/operations to be stored and the size of the internal CPU memory required. The number of part/operations within the net can be predicted by mul-

Sales Orders/ Forecast		Levels of BOM		Route Steps
1,000	×	5	×	7
Part/Operations		=		35,000

Figure 12.1   Determining the number of part/operations.

tiplying the number of sales order line items plus the forecast times the average levels within the bills of material by the average number of routing steps (see Figure 12.1). In the figure, there are 1000 line items between the sales orders on file and the forecast generated for the company, the average number of levels in the bills of material file is five, and there are an average of seven routing steps for each assembled item in the route file. In this case, the system should be sized to handle a total of 35,000 part/operations in the net.

Creating the interface and preparing the net

Systems currently available to support TOC based systems on a PC will include import tools. Import tools are software driven tools that will read specific data files downloaded from the host manufacturing system to the server or PC, consolidate the data and write the file contents to the net file.

Detail files will include the data discussed in Chapter 11, such as

- The order in which part/operations are processed
- Available inventory
- Resources
- Overtime availability
- Master schedule data

If this tool does not exist, it will need to be written. Chapter 11 presents in detail what data must be included in the net and from where it originates in the traditional manufacturing system.

Refreshing the net

How often the net needs to be refreshed depends on how dynamic the environment is. If significant changes are being made in the bill of material, routing or master schedule during the day and those changes need to be reflected in the schedule, then an update of the net on the server should be made in proportion to the rate of change that occurs. In the client/server environment shop floor data are being maintained at the server level. Thus, refreshing the net from the host as changes occur on the shop floor will not be necessary. It is only when changes occur on the host that the net must be refreshed from the host.

Changes occurring on the host manufacturing system which will result in a need to refresh the net are

- Old sales orders being filled and new ones added
- Changes in the forecast
- Bills of material and routings being updates
- New resources added and old ones deleted
- Changes in the due date of an order originating outside the system
- Significant changes in lead times for raw material
- Changes in setup or run time for those products which are processed on the constraint or on near-constraint resources

Note: an assumption is being made that the changes being made on the host will impact orders inside the time horizon for the schedule.

System security

Other than the normal security on the host system, there are three areas in which security will be a key issue:

- Making direct changes to the primary net on the server
- Creating and making changes to the schedule
- Shop floor reporting

The data residing on the server are the basis from which the net is imported to the client to support the decision process. It is important that these data remain the same for all who need access to make a decision. If for any reason the base net should be compromised, people could be making decisions based on different input. As an example, suppose that engineering were making a decision on buying a specific resource and increased the quantity of that resource on the net. When production control needs to schedule the factory, the environment will not resemble the current factory. Obviously, this is not an acceptable situation. There must be a method of password securing the primary net on the server so that only a few people have access to be able to add, change or delete it.

The capability to copy the net and create a new version which could be password secured by the individual user is also desirable. Users can thus examine several scenarios in which different shop floor environments are being used at the same time. Having access to numerous versions would save time by not having to constantly modify the same scenario over and over again to meet new changes.

Understanding where inventory is on the shop floor is necessary to effectively manage the shop and is also necessary as input to the scheduling process. Accuracy is critical. Access to material movement on the primary net should be password secured and limited to only those who are responsible for insuring that material is where it is supposed to be.

Testing the logic

In testing the system a subset of data should be used in a controlled environment to ensure that the system functions as desired. Once the interface is complete, choose specific data to enter and test. Make sure that the data selected for the test are representative of all testing scenarios to be performed. Start with the creation of the master schedule. Place one order on the MPS for a small amount so that it can be tracked through the creation of the net. Look at the descending part operation chart (see Figure 12.2).

Verify that every part/operation that is supposed to be in the net is there, that they appear in the proper sequence, and that each setup and run time is correct

Descending

S/O111 - A	
A/30	R-1
A/20	R-2
A/10	R-3
B/30	R-4
B/20	R-5
B/10	R-6
RM	C

Figure 12.2 Descending part/operation chart.

according to the data placed in the route file. Then place the orders on the timeline by creating the schedule. There will be only one, perhaps two, orders on any one resource, but it will be important to ensure that they appear on the timeline in the proper position given the buffer length for shipping and that functions such as off-loading to other resources works. Each order on the time line should be identified along with the setup and run times for each part/operation. Ensure that each resource can also be identified along with specific resource data.

During testing and in scheduling the factory, the system should permit manually identifying the constraint to force a schedule of a specific resource. Once the initial phase of testing is complete, expand the test to include a larger data set and manually identify the constraint. Check that each part/operation crossing the constraint has a start and stop time and that all rod types are in place and functioning. Figure 12.3 shows a feature that can be used to gain specific information about orders on the timeline. Notice that the applicable sales order, quantity, setup times, run times and start and stop times appear. Make sure that this data is correct based on manual mathematical computations.

The conference room pilot

The conference room pilot is the final test of the software and operating procedures prior to the physical implementation. It should be used to test the

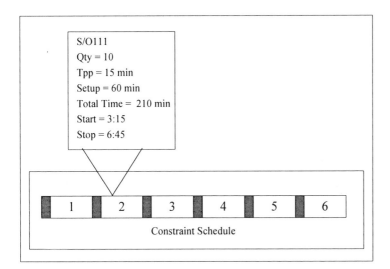

Figure 12.3 Testing the schedule.

ability of the software and procedures to accomplish the tasks they were designed to perform and should not be used as a test bed for MIS to ensure that the software actually works.

Every possible scenario should be tested, from scheduling the factory to making decisions. Although a tremendous amount of time will be spent trying, it is literally impossible to predict every situation. The number of issues that will emanate from the conference room pilot which were not predicted prior to developing the operating procedures will be amazing. That is one of the benefits in using the TOC thinking process discussed later in this chapter.

Included in the conference room pilot should be tests for specific functionality such as

- Generating the schedule for the constraint
- Looping back to the master schedule
- Handling rework and scrap
- Subordinating the activities of departments such as engineering, maintenance and quality
- Managing the buffer by reviewing its health indicators, controlling the buffer lengths and expediting past due orders
- Decision-making
- Moving material and entering data
- Focusing on improvements

The conference room pilot is absolutely essential in the success or failure of any system implementation. When attempting the kind of changes required by the theory of constraints, it becomes mandatory to test every aspect of the system prior to implementation.

The Physical Implementation

The physical implementation involves the interface with the users and the users' environment. It includes

- Modeling the plant
- Creating and following the schedule
- Buffer management

This begins the actual process of using the system to schedule the factory, focus the improvement process and make decisions.

Modeling the plant

The first step in the physical implementation is to model the plant. Modeling the plant means using the live data from the active host system to generate the net and to schedule the factory. The plant model is a view of how the facility might look if no policy constraints existed. The objective is not to use the data to sequence material flow within the factory, but to determine where the constraints are, where they should be and what must be done, if anything, to arrange the shape of the factory, such as placing the location of physical buffer areas.

The plant model also provides an excellent opportunity to view the impact of current non–TOC based policies on the profitability of the company. For example, what would be the impact if

- The correct products were being sold into the market
- The constraint was being exploited internally by maximizing its utilization
- Physical improvements were made prior to implementation which resulted in eliminating unresolvable conflicts between primary and secondary constraints

Modeling the plant is an extremely important step in the implementation of the TOC based system. It can provide some insight into the way things ought to be and can serve as a performance target.

The shop floor layout

A major change will occur in the way the factory appears. Figure 12.4 presents the suggested changes to the layout in which physical buffer areas are created based on certain characteristics. Notice that buffer areas have been prepared for the constraint, shipping and the assembly buffers. Since additional time is provided to allow material to arrive from the gating operations, orders will tend to collect in these areas. The shop should be prepared for this event and have specific space reserved. In addition, if enough material collects in these areas, a system may be needed to keep track of it. Specific attention should be paid to ensure that material to be processed on the buffer origin is readily available.

Once the conference room pilot has been completed and all procedures established for the use of the system, it is time to bring the implementation to the shop floor. Since all other processes such as buffer management and focus-

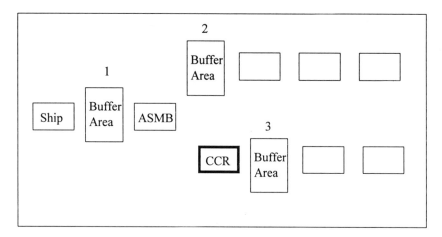

Figure 12.4   Suggested changes to the plant layout.

ing on improvements are dependent on the schedule, the primary issue will be to begin the process of identifying and scheduling the constraint. Prior to creating the schedule a trial buffer size should be used which is initially oversized. It will be obvious to buffer management that the buffer is too large. However, starting with an oversized buffer will ensure that the constraint is well protected when the process begins. The rule of thumb for the initial buffer length is three times the normal lead time. Once the system is stabilized and results become fairly predictable, begin shrinking the size of the buffers so that zones I and II reflect the desired rates.

It is important that the system reflects what is actually happening on the shop floor. Begin moving and reporting material between part/operations as it is completed.

Just because the system identifies a specific resource as the primary constraint does not mean that it is. There may be data accuracy issues which are preventing the system from processing correctly. Verify that the system is reporting what is actually happening on the shop floor. If material is collecting at a resource other than a constraint or the resource which has been identified as having limited capacity has no problem in keeping up with demand from other resources, begin investigating whether the data on these two resources is accurate. Since the system will permit the manual identification of the constraint, it is possible to establish a schedule for a resource which is giving physical signs of being the constraint, regardless of what the data may indicate.

Shrinking the size of the transfer batch

Companies using the repetitive manufacturing process or that have implemented Just-In-Time manufacturing systems have already been through the process of shrinking the transfer batch size. The best transfer batch size is a quantity of one. This is not to be confused with the process batch size. The best process batch size is one that maximizes utilization of the constraint. Most companies do not operate on this concept.

If the company is not currently operating with a transfer batch of one and it has been decided to make this transition, allow time during the implementation to master this technique. One of the toughest things to remember is that it is the buffer origins which must not run out of material. As inventories begin to fall and productivity increases, there will be an overwhelming urge on the part of some people who work at non-constraint resources to stay busy or to build ahead. The logical implementation will help tremendously.

The Logical Implementation

With 90% to 95% of the constraints to a company's making more money being other than a physical limitation, the probability is very high that after the system has been implemented the constraint will not have been broken. Nor does it guarantee that it will be broken in the future. The system will indicate that a physical constraint either does or does not exist and provide the basis for a valid decision process. However, even when these things are provided, it does not mean that the company will be guaranteed to make more money. Consistently implementing the five steps of improvement will.

Assuming that the technical and physical implementations have been successful, the primary issues involving implementation become

- The TOC decision process
- Dealing with the human interaction that will either enhance or block the successful implementation of the TOC based system
- Developing a successful implementation plan to support the implementation process

Overcoming Blocking Actions

Blocking occurs when a member of the company acts counter to the objective of the system. As an example, if a schedule is created on a resource which follows a diverging operation and a worker decides to work ahead in the schedule processing material which was to go to another part operation, then the actions of the worker will block the success of the company in maximizing its goal by mismatching parts.

Ensuring the success of the implementation requires educating people to inform them of the impact of their actions. It also requires a measurement system which will ensure that when blocking actions occur, that pressure will be exerted which will correct the situation.

Education

Oliver Wight was once quoted as saying, "If you think education is expensive you should try ignorance for a while." With a TOC based system people are more involved in the actual process of generating the schedule than with the traditional system. The usual procedure for MRP and CRP is to run a batch program and then generate a report or action messages when the system has finished its processing. The education process consists of defining what MRP or CRP are and how the system fits together. With a TOC based system the user is very much an active participant, making decisions at each step during the exploitation or subordination procedure. The user must answer questions such as

- Should setup savings be performed on a certain resource or should sales orders be pushed into the future? If the latter, which orders?
- Should overtime be applied? If so, where?
- What is the most profitable product mix given the current situation?
- Should the part be made on internal resources or purchased from an outside vendor?

This means that education is even more important in making the TOC system work. It's not so much what buttons to push that needs answering, but questions of a more dynamic nature. If the decision process is to change to the extent suggested and if the information system is to play a major role, then knowing how to make decisions using the information system also becomes an important factor.

What must be overcome is 50 to 100 years of an education and industrial system plagued by the almost dogmatic tendency to view every activity as an outlet of cost that must be improved. This one issue can destroy the implementation of the TOC based system. Education is crucial.

Because something is difficult does not mean it cannot or should not be done. Everyone who has spent a short time around the theory of constraints realizes that it's the only viable solution. Avoiding its implementation is like going to the doctor, being diagnosed with hepatitis and then not taking the medicine prescribed.

The first step in the implementation of the system must be to educate the people who use it either directly or indirectly. This includes anyone involved in the decision process, whether tactical or strategic, and anyone who must act on the decisions made by others. If production control produces a schedule and a foreman decides to maximize the utilization of all resources on the shop floor, then the schedule becomes useless. The foremen must understand the impact of what their actions are to the rest of the company.

Another example of a problem that can be created by the uninformed is the impact of irrational decisions with respect to market segmentation. If the markets fed by a specific resource chain are appropriately segmented and the chief financial officer decides that the company's resources should be split down product lines to more effectively manage cost, the segmentation process would be completely destroyed leaving the resource base exposed to market fluctuations.

Education of all employees within the company is imperative. In addition, after the process is complete the people must take ownership of the information transferred. There are two issues:

- The education process must be of such a nature that it causes people to change of their own volition.
- The education process must be followed by a change in the measurement system. If the measurement system is not changed, then people will not change. They will continue to maximize the measurements they are given.

Note: a good resource for understanding the measurements systems and the changes required can be found in Lockamy and Cox's *Re-Engineering Performance Measurement* (1994).

In the case where the constraint is constantly being elevated, there is a good chance that eventually it will arrive at the office of someone who does not understand the impact of implementing the five steps or who may even be hostile to the prospect of leaving the cost world methodologies. Many arguments have resulted from the lack of understanding on the part of key people within numerous companies. These people must be educated immediately so that the process does not stop. In many cases, the emphasis necessary to convince some people to listen will come from the office of the president.

The permanent education program

As people leave the company and are replaced, new employees will be coming from environments where cost accounting is the primary driver. It is amazing how many people are still uninformed. Even people who have made the transition to the cost world will need refresher training or training in other areas as their careers progress. This requires that a permanent education program be established.

Educational requirements for the implementation of the TOC based information system include

- The cost world versus the throughput world
- The concept of "continuous profit improvement"
- Understanding the decision process
- Drum-buffer-rope (DBR)
- The information system
- The TOC thinking process

Examination of the cost world versus throughput world is designed to bring users to the obvious conclusion that a change must be made in how companies are run and in the decision process. Understanding the decision process is more complex and may need to be explained in the context of the job to be performed. Training the shop floor supervisor how to make sales decisions may be a waste of time.

As presented in Chapter 13 of *The Next Phase of Total Quality Management* (1994) specific educational requirements for the implementation of the DBR process include

- How resources interface
- How a schedule should be generated
- What the rules of resource activation are
- How material releases are determined
- What the five steps are in the process of continuous improvement

- How to exploit the constraint
- How to properly subordinate
- How to make decisions

A list of these kinds of issues should be created for each departmental function for the company and education sessions performed.

Simulation as a training tool

When making this kind of a change, one of the best methods is to place the individual in the environment in which he or she must perform and present the outcome of the decisions made. This process is best done through simulation. The simulator can be used to educate people in a number of different areas, including

- Quality
- Cost accounting
- Resource maintenance
- Setup reduction
- Purchasing
- Product design
- Market segmentation
- Growing the company

Figure 12.5 is representative of how a simulator for the manufacturing environment might appear. Each resource type is represented by a specific pattern. Notice that resource types R-2, R-3 and R-4 have a quantity of two. Each resource is connected from the gating operation to the sales order through specific part operations. Raw material enters the process from the left and appears in circles. Finished products F and G leave the process from the right. A specific part/operation is found by an intersection of the numbers appearing down the left side and the letters appearing across the top. The last part/operation before product F is shipped is 3/D and is processed on resource R-5. Notice also that certain part/operations have inventory. Part/operation 7/A has twenty Ks ready to process while 1/B has ten 1/As to process. Part/operation 4/C has only some of its parts required to begin processing. It has ten 5/Bs and needs ten 3/Bs as well. The objective of this screen is to simulate the decisions made by the user and to predict an outcome based on the physical interfaces and characteristics of each resource.

Depending on the decision to be made additional information will be needed. Figure 12.6A is a list of the resources and their available statistics. Notice that

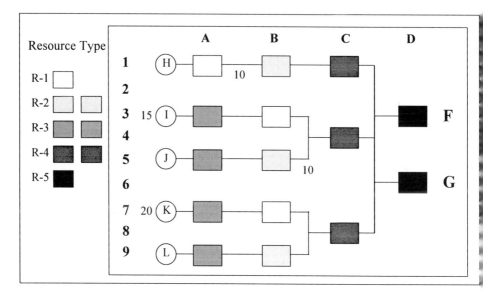

Figure 12.5   The education simulator.

the scrap rate for R-3 is 15% and that R-1 has a scrap rate of 3%, and that downtime and rework are also listed.

To complete the picture will require data on the amount of setup and run time for a specific part/operation and the demand placed on the system through sales orders (see Figure 12.6B). Now that all the data are available, the student can be led through different methodologies focusing on the different processes, such as total productive maintenance or single minute exchange of die. Decision processes such as make/buy or scrap/rework can be worked out just as easily.

When the decision to take a specific action such as reducing the amount of rework at resource R-1 or R-4, the student can learn the impact of the decision on throughput, inventory and operating expense after running the simulation and looking at the final profitability statistics (see Figure 12.7).

The student can make repairs to specific resources or products based on cost accounting then use TOC based throughput accounting. Different actions will result in an increase or decrease to throughput, inventory or operating expense. To repair a resource causes operating expense to increase and, therefore, there must also be an increase in throughput or the company looses money.

Resources	Time Available	Down Time	Scrap Rate	Rework Rate
R-1	480	0%	3%	5%
R-2	960	10%	0%	0%
R-3	960	0%	15%	0%
R-4	480	0%	0%	15%
R-5	480	25%	0%	0%

(A)

Part/Op.	Setup	Run
1/A	30	10
3/A	15	3
5/A	60	5
7/A	30	10
9/A	100	5
1/B	15	2
3/B	30	15
5/B	60	5
7/B	45	10
9/B	50	5

Part/Op.	Setup	Run
1/C	30	5
4/C	60	10
8/C	60	5
3/D	30	3
6/D	15	12

Product	QTY	Due
F	100	251
G	150	251
F	50	254
G	50	255
F	100	255
F	100	256

(B)

Figure 12.6 (A) Resource data. (B) Part/operation data.

This kind of an educational tool is extremely valuable in developing an education program designed to change the perspective of those who must run the company on a day-to-day basis. It should be available in every TOC managed company and considered part of the requirements for a permanent education program.

	Beginning	Ending
Throughput: $32,000	Inventory: $63,000	$57,000
Operating Expense: $10,000		

Return On Investment: .20

Net Profit: $12,000

Productivity: 3.2

Inventory Turns: .53

Figure 12.7 The bottom line results of the decision after running the simulation.

Using the TOC based system as a training aid

Completing the conceptual education, the next phase of education should include training on the TOC based system by placing the student in the actual environment in which he or she is to perform. Using a copy or subset of the actual environment as a training aid is excellent for insuring that the student can move from the conceptual world to reality.

In generating the course curriculum the instructor should develop specific scenarios involving the decision process for each functional department. Each scenario would involve a specific decision under a given set of circumstances, such as:

- Establishing the correct product mix
- Making or buying a certain product
- Generating the schedule
- Setup reduction

Under certain circumstances increasing the productivity of a specific resource may cause more problems in being able to resolve conflict between schedules on the primary and secondary constraint. Properly presented, the student will readily see the impact of his or her decisions on the schedule and understand the impact of individual decisions on the three measurements of throughput inventory and operating expense.

The measurement system

As mentioned earlier, education must be followed by a change in the measurement system to reinforce the desire to act in a manner consistent with the goal of the corporation. If an action such as releasing or processing material earlier than required by the schedule will result in a negative impact on the company by increasing inventory, then whenever this activity occurs a measurement system must exist which will immediately alert the company to undesirability activity. Detailed information on measurement systems can be found in

- *The Haystack Syndrome* (1990)
- *The Next Phase of Total Quality Management*
- *Re-Engineering Performance Measurements*

DEVELOPING THE IMPLEMENTATION PLAN

The implementation of a TOC based system is very much different than for an MRP system. With TOC, there are the added problems associated with understanding and executing the new decision process as well as eliminating invalid policies. However, invalid policies do not announce themselves. They only appear as undesirable effects. After everyone has been educated, the integration process is completed and the schedule created there is no guarantee that the implementation will be a success. As an example, what would be the impact if for some reason the constraint kept moving from resource to resource even though everyone was trying their best to follow the schedule? The TOC thinking process is used to ensure that invalid policies can be found and solutions devised to eliminate them. Thus, in developing the implementation plan there are two issues:

- Those activities designed to implement the system
- Those activities which are necessary to eliminate invalid policies which serve to block a successful implementation

The implementation plan is a plan of action which defines what is to be done, who is to do it and when it is to take place. Those activities common to every plan for implementing the TOC based system are

- Begin the education process.
- Re-write the corporate policy book.
- Complete the integration to the standard manufacturing system.

- Establish the test net.
- Test the logic.
- Model the plant.
- Determine and execute the plant layout.
- Write the procedures.
- Develop the conference room pilot scenario.
- Execute the conference room pilot.
- Develop and execute the education and training sessions.
- Determine the buffer sizes.
- Determine overtime and setup savings limitations.
- Create the master schedule.
- Develop the initial schedule.
- Execute the schedule.
- Begin the buffer management process.
- Begin TOC decision support.
- Begin TOC thinking process support—help to generate the road map.

Note: re-writing the corporate policy book includes generating a set of general instructions designed to ensure that managers will use, as their guiding principles, the methodologies and decision models originating from the theory of constraints.

Each TOC system implementation will have activities that are very different. For every company, problems will occur that will tend to block a successful implementation. While these activities may have common causes, they will manifest themselves in very different ways. The TOC thinking process is the road map used to guide the implementation process through those activities.

The TOC Thinking Process

The objective of the TOC thinking process is to define those actions necessary to improve a company given the current situation and to guide each step to its sometimes not so obvious conclusion. It defines

- What to change
- What to change to
- How to accomplish the change

Defined in *It's Not Luck* (1994) and included in the TOC thinking process are five tools:

- The currently reality tree (CRT)—used to find the core cause or causes from undesirable effects
- Evaporating clouds (EC) (assumption model)—used to model the assumptions made which block the creation of a breakthrough solution
- The future reality tree (FRT)—used to model the changes created after defining breakthrough changes from the evaporating cloud
- The prerequisite tree (PT)—used to uncover and solve intermediate obstacles to achieving the goal
- The transition tree (TT)—used to define those actions necessary to achieve the goal

The TOC thinking process is used to guide the implementation of the theory of constraints and to aid in creating breakthrough solutions. This can also be of tremendous benefit to the implementation of the TOC based system by ensuring that any undesirable effects which manifest themselves during the implementation process are eliminated.

Note: an excellent reference for the TOC thinking process is *The Theory of Constraints and Its Implications for Management Accounting* (1995).

The current reality tree

The first step in the execution of the TOC thinking process is to list the undesirable effects (UDEs) and then create the current reality tree. The current reality tree is a diagram built on the cause and effect relationships between the undesirable effects and their immediate causes. The objective is to find the core cause. Once found and eliminated, all undesirable effects should disappear.

If the core cause can be found and a solution implemented, then these effects should no longer exist. If they continue, then the core cause(s) was not eliminated. As an example, the following are undesirable effects that may occur during an implementation of the system and can be used to build a current reality tree:

UDE-1: Resource R-3 often receives mismatched parts from R-4.
UDE-2: Sales orders are frequently shipped late for product A.
UDE-3: Resource R-2 often has holes in zone I of the buffer caused by late orders for part/operation A/10.
UDE-4: Part/operations B/30 and D/30 are often expedited from R-4.
UDE-5: There are holes in zone I of the shipping buffer for product A.

UDE-6: R-4 is consistently working overtime to supply parts D/30 and
B/30.

Notice that each UDE has been numbered. This is done so that each UDE can be
easily identified in the current reality trees to follow. Figure 12.8 is the product
flow diagram in which the previously defined UDEs exist.

Note: the product flow diagram is not part of the thinking process. It has been
supplied as a reference point for the discussion of the five tools.

In Figure 12.9, UDE-2 is the first undesirable effect to be placed and appears at
the head of the arrow. In other words, it is the identifiable effect and can be
related directly to the text in block one. Block one and all blocks numbered in
the same fashion are known as "entities." To read the diagram the block at the
tale of the arrow is read first. The tale of the arrow is identified with the word *if*,
while the head of the arrow is identified with the word *then*. So, the relationship
between UDE-2 and entity 1 should read

> **if:**   (entity 1) product A is frequently late arriving from production,
> **then:** (UDE-2) sales orders are frequently shipped late for product A.

Entity 1 is also connected to UDE-5:

> **if:**   (entity 1) product A is frequently late arriving from production,
> **then:** (UDE-5) there are holes in the zone one of the shipping buffer for product A.

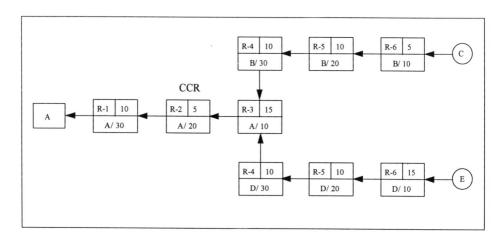

Figure 12.8   The product flow diagram for product A.

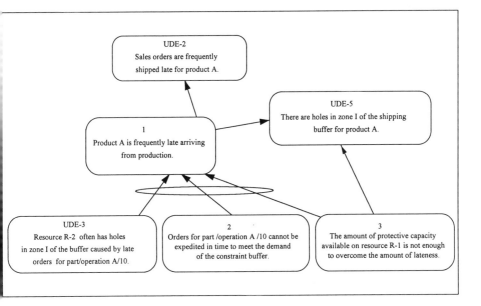

Figure 12.9 Current reality tree.

Note: the process of identifying relationships between UDEs and entities continues until the core cause is discovered.

UDE-3 is also connected to entity 1. However, UDE-3 is at the tale of the arrow. There is now a connection between UDEs 2, 3 and 5 through entity 1:

    if: (UDE-3) resource R-2 often has holes in zone I of the buffer caused by late orders for part/operation A/10,

  then: (entity 1) product A is frequently arriving late from production.

Notice that this statement cannot necessarily stand by itself. Just because there are holes in the buffer for product A does not mean that product A will be frequently late in arriving from production. There must be supporting causes. Entity 2 states that orders for part/operation A/10 cannot be expedited in time to meet the demand of the constraint buffer.

Note: the constraint has been identified in the product flow diagram as R-2.

The arrows originating from UDE-3 and entity 2 are joined by an ellipse along with entity 3. In this case the relationship is read:

if: (UDE-3) resource R-2 often has holes in zone I of the buffer caused by late orders for part/operation A/10,

and if: (entity 2) orders for part/operation A/10 cannot be expedited in time to meet the demand of the constraint buffer,

and if: (entity 3) the amount of protective capacity available in resource R-1 is not enough to overcome the amount of lateness,

then: (entity 1) product A is frequently arriving late from production.

In this case, there is enough evidence to point to a definite cause and effect relationship between entity 1, UDE-3, entity 2 and entity 3.

Once constructed the current reality tree can provide tremendous insight into the cause and effect relationships of activities occurring throughout the plant. While it is developed from the undesirable effects and projects downward toward the core causes, the current reality tree can, and should, be validated by reading from the bottom up. Entity 14 in Figure 12.10 has been identified as the core cause for creating the late orders. When combined with entity 15 there is sufficient cause and effect relationship to justify entity 7.

if: (entity 14) R-4 is combining lots to save setup,

and if: (entity 15) R-4 has not been identified as a secondary constraint and a schedule produced to subordinate R-4 to R-2,

then: (entity 7) R-4 is not producing B/30 and D/30 according to schedule.

The issue now turns to understanding why setup savings are being performed for part/operations B/30 and D/30 at resource R-4. Before a successful plan can be adopted a basic understanding of why is important. Short of asking the foreman, a basic analysis should be performed.

Note: asking the foreman why he is performing setup savings on a non-constraint resource may solidify his insistence to continue.

Figure 12.11 presents one reason that the foreman may be acting as he is. Beginning at the bottom it reads

if: (entity 18) people will act based on how they are measured,

and if: (entity 19) R-4 is measured based on productivity,

then: (entity 17) the actions of people at R-4 will be to maximize the productivity at R-4.

Continuing to the next level, the diagram reads:

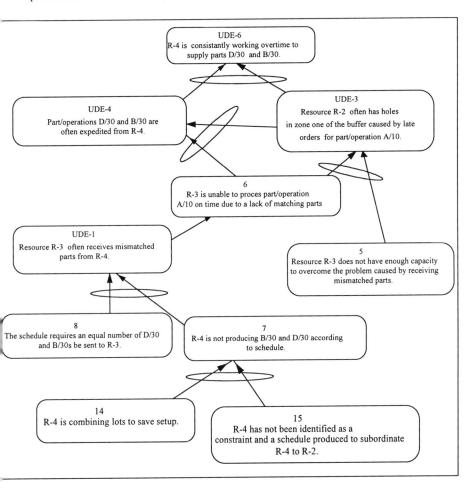

Figure 12.10 Current reality tree.

    if: (entity 17) the actions of people at R-4 will be to maximize the productivity at R-4,

and if: (entity 20) setup savings is a way to maximize productivity,

  then: (entity 22) R-4 will combine lots to save set up and maximize productivity.

So the core cause for the setup savings occurring on a non-constraint resource may be due to how the foreman is being measured externally (a managerial constraint), or in how he measures himself (a behavioral constraint).

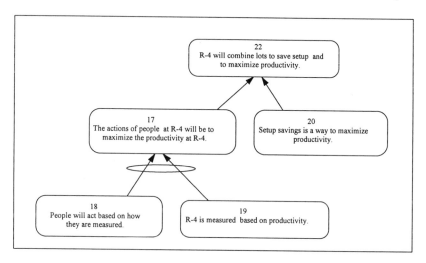

Figure 12.11 Current reality tree.

Creating the Evaporating Cloud

As stated earlier, the evaporating cloud is used to model the assumptions made which block the creation of a breakthrough solution. Figure 12.12 represents an evaporating cloud. Notice that the objective of the model is placed on the left at position A. The objective may be to increase return on investment. Positions B

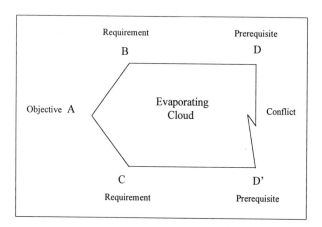

Figure 12.12 The evaporating cloud.

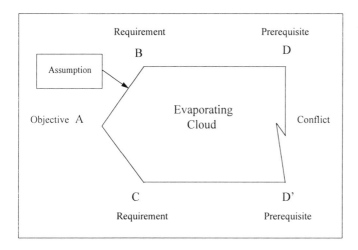

Figure 12.13 The evaporating cloud—assumption placement.

and C represent those things that are required in order to meet the objective. Position B might read "increase productivity" and position C might read "exploit the constraint." Positions D and D' represent the conflict. In other words there is an assumption that D and D' cannot exist together.

The cloud reads as follows:

- In order to have A there must be B.
- In order to have A there must be C.
- A prerequisite to B is that there must be D.
- A prerequisite to C is that there must be D'.
- D and D' cannot exist together.

To solve a problem involving the evaporating cloud the assumptions made between each of the entries in the cloud are examined for possible flaws. In Figure 12.13, in order to say that there is a relationship between A and B there must be certain assumptions made such as the only way to have A is to first have B. If the assumption can be proven false, then the problem evaporates.

The foreman's dilemma: evaporating the cloud

Figure 12.14 represents the foreman's dilemma. In this case the objective is to increase return on investment. The foreman's cloud reads as follows:

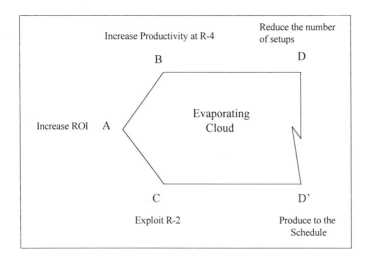

Figure 12.14   Evaporating cloud example.

- A-B: In order to increase return on investment, productivity at R-4 must be increased.
- A-C: In order to increase return on investment, R-2 must be exploited.
- B-D: In order to increase productivity at R-4, the number of setups must be reduced.
- C-D': In order to exploit R-2, R-4 must produce to the schedule.
- D-D': Producing to the schedule set for R-2 and saving setup are mutually exclusive.

To solve the foreman's dilemma the first step is to list the assumptions being made between the entries. Most of the time there will be more than one assumption made. Our assumptions are

- A-B: There is a direct relationship between the local measurement of productivity at R-4 and the global measurement of return on investment.
- A-C: Exploiting R-2 throughput will increase, thereby causing ROI to increase.
- B-D: Setup savings at R-4 can only have a positive impact.
- C-D': R-4 must be subordinated to the demand created by R-2.
- D-D': There is no way that R-4 can follow the schedule for R-2 and perform setup savings at the same time.

A-B makes the assumption that there is a direct relationship between the increased productivity at resource R-4 and the increase in return on investment. This assumption is not necessarily true. Improving at a non-constraint resource from a global perspective will not cause throughput to increase. B-D also has a problem. As seen later, saving setup on a non-constraint resource will often subvert the schedule of the constraint causing ROI to decrease rather than increase. If setup savings is not performed in direct synchronization with the constraint's schedule, then there is a good chance that the constraint schedule will be invalidated by the setup process. This is a key issue in solving the foreman's dilemma.

The Future Reality Tree

As defined earlier, the future reality tree is used to model the changes created after defining the breakthrough solution from the evaporating cloud. In this case, a new measurement system is being provided to the foreman (see Figures 12.15 to 12.17). The future reality tree is built starting with what is called an *injection* and is read in the same manner as the current reality tree. An injection is the change designed to solve the undesirable effects. In this case, the injection is to measure foreman performance based on throughput dollar days. The future reality tree reads as follows.

    if: (injection 1) the foreman's performance is measured based on throughput dollar days accumulated,
then: (entity 26) pressure on the foreman to deliver parts according to the schedule for R-2.

and

    if: (entity 26) pressure increases on the foreman to deliver parts according to the schedule for R-2,
and if: (entity 27) the schedule for R-2 is communicated to R-4 through the release schedule for R-6,
  then: (entity 28) R-4 will begin to process orders as they are received first in (first out [FIFO]).

Notice that entity 29 is a desirable effect (DE). This means that the entity is the exact opposite of the undesirable effect from the UDE list. In this case, one of the undesirable effects has been eliminated by the change in the way foreman performance is measured.

    if: (entity 28) R-4 begins to process orders FIFO,
 then: (DE-29) R-3 will receive matching parts from R-4.

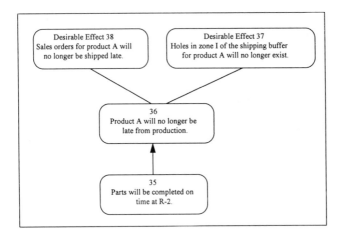

Figure 12.15 Future reality tree.

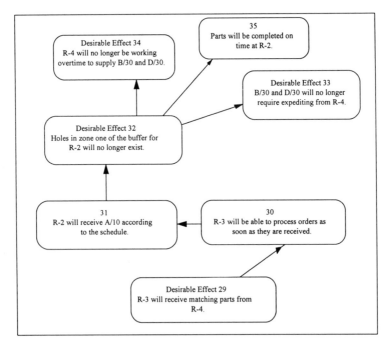

Figure 12.16 Future reality tree.

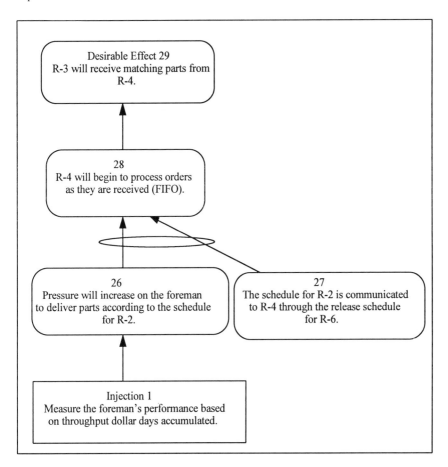

Figure 12.17 Future reality tree.

Notice that in the remainder of the current reality tree all of the undesirable effects have been eliminated, including UDE-2 (sales orders are frequently shipped late for product A) and replaced by desirable effects.

The foreman's dilemma: trimming the negative branches

Somehow the solution does not seem complete. If the measurement system was not the only issue which prevented the foreman from following the schedule, then the devised solution may not replace all the undesirable effects with

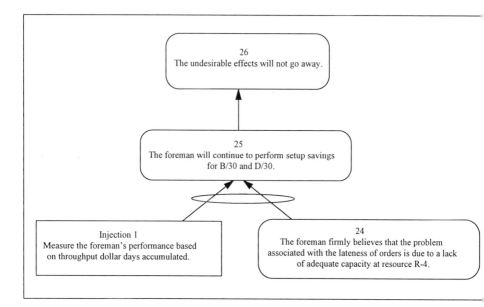

Figure 12.18 Future reality tree showing reservations to solution.

desirable effects as defined in the future reality tree. At this point all reservations should be surfaced as to the validity of the solution. Figure 12.18 serves to illustrate the reservation. The following can be inferred:

      if: (injection 1) the foreman's performance is measured based on throughput dollar days accumulated,

and if: (entity 27) the foreman firmly believes that the problem associated with the lateness of orders is due to a lack of adequate capacity at resource R-4,

  then: (entity 25) the foreman will continue to perform setup savings for B/30 and D/30.

      if: (entity 25) the foreman continues to perform setup savings for B/30 and D/30,

  then: (entity 26) the undesirable effects will not go away.

Revisiting the foreman's dilemma

From Figure 12.18 it is learned that there is a distinct possibility that the foreman firmly believes that the undesirable effects are caused by the fact that there is not enough capacity at R-4. Merely placing a new measurement system

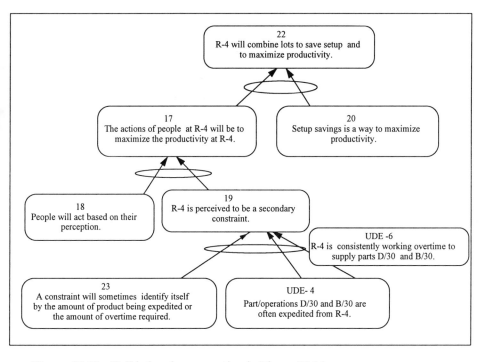

Figure 12.19   Validating the reservation in Figure 12.18.

in this environment may only serve to exacerbate the situation. Figure 12.19 defines another possible cause for the setup savings. It reads as follows:

> **if:**   (entity 23) a constraint will sometimes identify itself by the amount of product being expedited or the amount of overtime required,
> **and if:**   (UDE-4) part/operations D/30 and B/30 are often expedited from R-4,
> **and if:**   (UDE-6) R-4 is consistently working overtime to supply parts D/30 and B/30,
> **then:**   (entity 19) R-4 is perceived to be a secondary constraint.

> **if:**   (entity 18) people act based on their perception,
> **and if:**   (entity 19) R-4 is perceived to be a secondary constraint,
> **then:**   (entity 17) the actions of people at R-4 will be to maximize the productivity at R-4.

> **if:**   (entity 17) the actions of people at R-4 will be to maximize the productivity at R-4,
> **and if:**   (entity 20) setup savings is a way to maximize productivity,
> **then:**   (entity 22) R-4 will combine lots to save setup and to maximize productivity.

Expanding the Future Reality Tree

To solve the new problem the future reality tree must be expanded to include a new entity. The bottom of the future reality tree now reads

      if: (injection 1) the foreman's performance is measured based on throughput dollar days accumulated,
  then: (entity 26) pressure will increase on the foreman to deliver parts according to the schedule for R-2.

      if: (entity 26) pressure increases on the foreman to deliver parts according to the schedule for R-2,
and if: (entity 27) the schedule for R-2 is communicated to R-4 through the release schedule for R-6,
and if: (entity 40) the foreman believes that R-4 is not a secondary constraint,
  then: (entity 28) R-4 will begin to process orders FIFO.

See Figure 12.20.

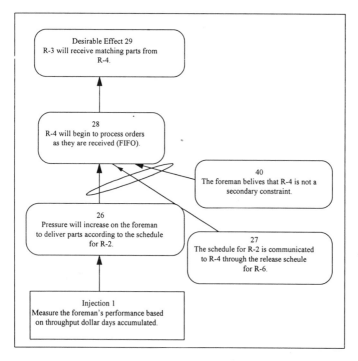

Figure 12.20 Recognizing the new entity.

So in order for the problem to be solved, the foreman must believe that R-4 is not a secondary constraint. A new injection must be introduced that will cause the foreman to change this belief. Assuming that the implementation of the system has included education and training, for the foreman should already be aware of the impact of setup savings on a non-constraint resource. The solution may be in providing a method for the foreman to simulate the current environment to either validate or disprove the belief.

Note: this issue serves to underline the need for the permanent education program so that people can invent their own solutions.

Simulating the Foreman's Problem

Figure 12.21 defines why the parts arriving at R-3 are mismatched. If setup savings is performed on R-4, some of the orders will be pushed outward in time while others will be pulled in. The result is that R-4, which had been synchronized to the constraint schedule of R-2 by the release schedule for R-6, will no longer be synchronized. According to the schedule in the figure, R-3 will receive large batches of B/30 and then large batches of D/30. The foreman begins working overtime to keep up with material expedited to R-3 and concludes that there is not enough available capacity to remedy the situation. This a normal conclusion and is made every day in the traditional MRP facility.

This is exactly the kind of information that can induce a change in the foreman's activity. Fortunately the TOC based system is capable of simulating the interface requirements between R-2 and R-4. If the constraint schedule has been created for R-2 and it becomes necessary to determine the impact on R-4, R-4 can be declared a secondary constraint. Orders are then placed on the time line

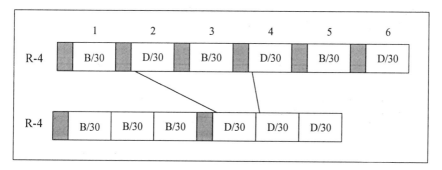

Figure 12.21 Simulating the foreman's problem.

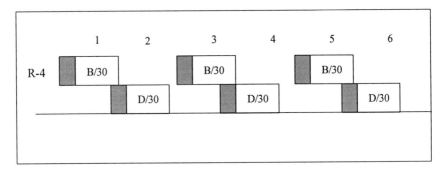

Figure 12.22 Placing orders on the time line for R-4.

in synchronization to R-2. If a conflict does not exist between orders on the time line for R-4 prior to generating a schedule for R-4, the chances are great that there is more than enough capacity to handle the demand generated by R-2. If any conflicts exist, they will surface as two part/operations trying to occupy the same space at the same time on the time line for R-4 (see Figure 12.22). Notice that orders 1 and 2 are trying to occupy the same space on the time line. However, this does not mean that there is a problem. To understand the issue under this condition a schedule needs to be created for R-4 (see Figure 12.23).

If the system places orders so that there are no gaps between orders (additional time), this is an indication that R-4's time is limited. If there are no late orders and setup savings is not indicated on the system, then chances are good that setup savings is not required on the shop floor either. Gaps between orders on the schedule for R-4 are an indication that there is plenty of additional time and that the foreman's assumption that R-4 should be declared a secondary constraint and setup savings performed is false (see Figure 12.24). Notice that there is a gap between the start of the planning horizon and the start of order 1. Notice also that there are gaps between orders 2 and 3 as well as orders 4 and 5.

Figure 12.23 Generating the schedule.

Figure 12.24 Gaps between orders.

Adding the New Injections

There are actually two new injections which are necessary to induce the foreman to stop setup savings at R-4 (see Figure 12.25):

  if: (injection 2) the foreman is provided with a method to simulate the environment,
and if: (entity 43) the simulation indicates that R-4 is not the constraint,
  then: (entity 40) the foreman will believe that R-4 is not a secondary constraint.

Figure 12.26 contains injection 3.

  if: (injection 3) the foreman is provided with training in the DBR process,
then: (entity 41) the foreman will understand the impact of setup savings on a non-constraint resource.

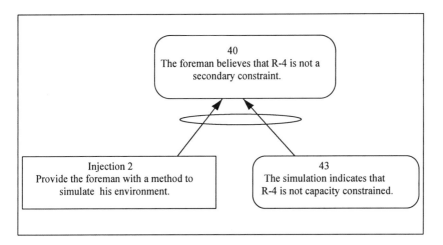

Figure 12.25 Adding injection 2 to the future reality tree.

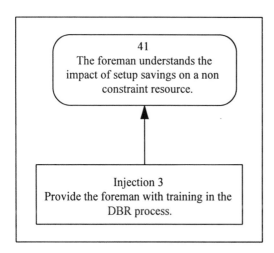

Figure 12.26   Adding injection 3 to the future reality tree.

In Figure 12.27, the bottom of the future reality tree now reads:

    if: (entity 26) pressure will increase on the foreman to deliver parts according to schedule,

and if: (entity 27) the schedule for R-2 is communicated to R-4 through the release schedule for R-6,

and if: (entity 40) the foreman believes that R-4 is not the secondary constraint,

and if: (entity 41) the foreman understands the impact of setup savings on a non-constraint resource,

   then: (entity 28) R-4 will begin to process orders FIFO.

The Prerequisite Tree

As stated earlier, the objective of the prerequisite tree (PT) is to uncover and solve intermediate obstacles to achieving the goal. The injections from the future reality tree are used to guide the process. As each injection is presented, obstacles to its realization surface. The intermediate objective in attaining the injection is to overcome the obstacle.

The injection is usually placed at the top of the diagram in a rectangle, the obstacle is placed to the left contained in a hexagon, while the intermediate objective is contained in a rounded rectangle.

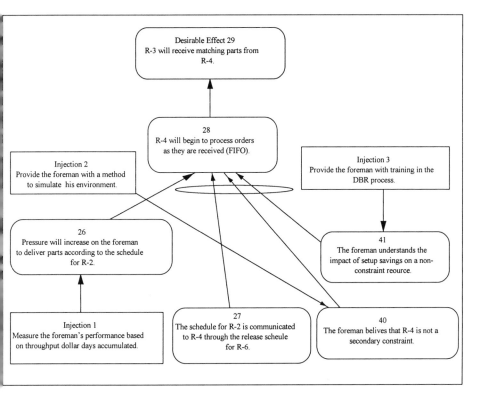

Figure 12.27 Expanding the future reality tree.

Figure 12.28 involves injection 1 (measure the foreman's performance based on throughput dollar days accumulated). Notice that one of the obstacles (obstacle 2) to attaining injection 1 is that the foreman may not understand the benefit of the T$D measurement process. This could easily derail the benefits of using the new measurement system. The other obstacle (obstacle 4) to attaining injection one is that the tools necessary to collect and manipulate the T$D data for the new measurement system are not available. To overcome the obstacle the intermediate objective is used. The intermediate objective is the exact opposite of the obstacle. The intermediate objective to overcome obstacle 2 is that the foreman understands the measurement system. The opposite of obstacle 4 is that the tools are available. It now becomes clear that in order to obtain injection 1, action must be taken to make sure that the foreman understands the measurement system and that tools be made available to collect data.

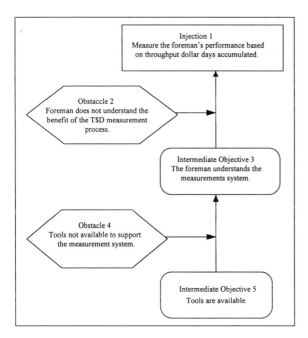

Figure 12.28 The prerequisite tree.

In Figure 12.29 the obstacle to attaining injection 2 is that the foreman will not know how to use the tool. The intermediate objective is that the foreman does know how to use the simulation tool.

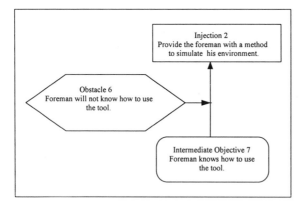

Figure 12.29 The prerequisite tree.

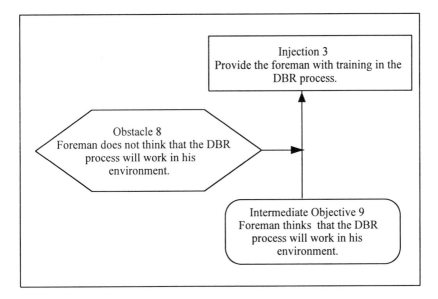

Figure 12.30 The prerequisite tree.

In Figure 12.30 the obstacle to attaining injection three is that the foreman does not think that the DBR process will work in this environment. The intermediate objective is that the foreman thinks the DBR process will work in this environment.

The Transition Tree

As defined earlier, the transition tree is used to define those actions necessary to achieve the goal. Like the prerequisite tree, the transition tree begins with the injection (see Figure 12.31). The intermediate objectives are listed to the left in the rounded rectangular boxes and the actions designed to attain the intermediate objective are placed in rectangles. The arrows designate which actions apply to the intermediate objective. In order to attain intermediate objective 5 action 1 must take place. In order to have intermediate objective 3 action 2 must take place.

The two actions required to attain the intermediate objectives as well as injection 1 include training the foreman to understand the measurement system and creating the tools to collect and manipulate the T$D data from the shop floor.

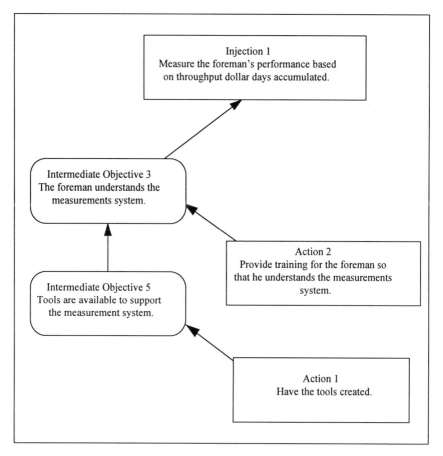

Figure 12.31 The transition tree.

In Figure 12.32 the action required to insure that the foreman believes that the DBR process will work in this environment (action 3) is to use the Socratic method with the educational simulators in the permanent education program and re-create the foreman's environment during education.

The action required to insure that the foreman knows how to use the simulation tool is (action 4) train the foreman to use the simulator (see Figure 12.33).

The TOC thinking process (TP) has been used successfully in companies around the world to create solutions to very complex problems. Using TP to aid in the implementation of the manufacturing information system is a logical extension.

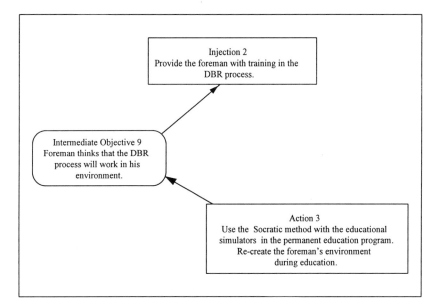

Figure 12.32 The transition tree.

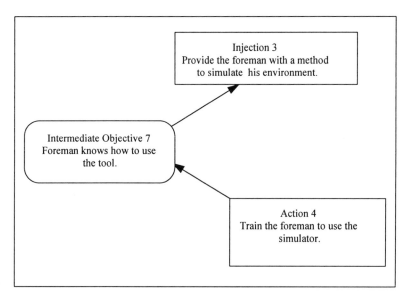

Figure 12.33 The transition tree.

Using the System to Develop the Road Map

Since the system is an excellent representation of reality and is devoid of policy constraints, it can be an excellent tool for helping to develop and execute the road map. As an example, the physical environment and its attributes will have a significant impact on solutions provided by the road map. The information system will not only inform the user what the impact of the physical attributes might be, but can also be used to test specific changes suggested in the creation of a breakthrough solution and will also aid in its execution.

The following list suggests ways in which the system can be used in support of the generation of the road map:

- Current reality tree—does excess capacity exist? If so, where?
- Break through solution—testing assumptions.
- Future reality tree—if a specific action is taken, what are the results?
- Prerequisite tree—if a specific goal is identified (e.g., conflicts between resources), what intermediate obstacles will block attaining the goal?

SUMMARY

As indicated throughout the text, the TOC, "haystack compatible" system represents a tremendous paradigm shift from the traditional approach and, as such, will change the way companies operate for years to come. Based on reality, the TOC information system solves a tremendous number of logistical and policy constraints that have hampered the effective use of the computer based information system since its development more than 30 years ago. Implemented correctly and used to its fullest extent it can be a tremendous asset in support of any manufacturing company.

STUDY QUESTIONS

1. Why is a TOC based manufacturing system more difficult to implement than a traditional system?

2. Define a successful TOC system implementation.

3. What preparations should be made to prevent failure?

4. Explain the uses and benefits of the permanent education program.

5. What is the TOC thinking process and what advantage does it provide to the implementation process?

6. List and define the five thinking tools.

7. What primary issue will tend to block most implementations and how can it be prevented?

8. Why is simulation such a great training aid? How should it be used?

9. What key issues are involved in selecting the computer system to run the TOC based software? Why?

10. What is the benefit provided by the conference room pilot and what issues should be stressed?

11. What is meant by the terms *technical, physical* and *logical implementation*?

12. What is the first step in the physical implementation and what is its objective?

13. What changes occurring on the host manufacturing system result in the need to refresh the net?

14. Develop a complete road map using the TOC thinking process to analyze and solve a problem in your life where your intuition is relatively mature.

15. Define the following terms as they relate to the TOC thinking process:

- Entity
- Reservation
- Undesirable effect
- Desirable effect
- Intermediate objective
- Action
- Obstacle

Bibliography

Goldratt, Eliyahu M., and Robert F. Fox, *The Race*, North River Press, Croton-on-Hudson, NY (1986).

Goldratt, Eliyahu M., *The Haystack Syndrome*, North River Press, Croton-on-Hudson, NY (1990).

Goldratt, Eliyahu M., and Jeff Cox, *The Goal*, North River Press, Great Barrington, MA (1992).

Goldratt, Eliyahu M., *It's Not Luck*, North River Press, Great Barrington, MA (1995).

Lockamy, Archie, and James F. Cox, *Re-Engineering Performance Measurements*, Irwin Professional Publishing, New York (1994).

Noreen, Eric, Debra Smith, and James T. Mackey, *The Theory of Constraints and Its Implications for Management Accounting*, North River Press, Great Barrington, MA (1995).

Orlicky, Joseph, *Material Requirements Planning*, McGraw-Hill Book Company, New York (1974).

Stein, Robert E., *The Next Phase of Total Quality Management: TQM II and the Focus on Profitability*, Marcel Dekker, Inc., New York (1994).

Umble, Michael M., and M. L. Srikanth, *Synchronous Manufacturing*: *Principles of World Class Excellence*, Southwestern Publishing Co., Cincinnati, OH (1990).

Vollman, Thomas E., William L. Berry, and D. Clay Whybark, *Manufacturing Planning and Control Systems*, Dow Jones Irwin, Homewood, IL (1988).

Glossary of TOC Terms

Action   An activity defined in a transition tree which is used to obtain an intermediate objective.

Activation   The employment of a non-constraint resource for the sake of keeping busy. Activation is unrelated to whether it is useful in supporting system throughput (APICS).

Additional cause   In the TOC thinking process, an additional cause is used when the presumed cause by itself is insufficient to explain the existence of an effect.

Aggregation of demand   The result of the use of the formula capacity divided by demand in which all demand is aggregated into time buckets. The assumption is made that all capacity is available to all demand within the time bucket.

A-plant   The A-plant is characterized by a large number of converging operations that start with a wide variety of raw material items being assembled in succeeding levels to create a smaller number of end items.

Artificial demand   A feature of the dynamic buffering process, artificial demand originates from internal processing logic. It is demand placed on a resource to protect available capacity when a certain number of consecutive periods on a resource have been schedule at 100% by external demand.

Ascending part/operations list   A feature of the system which lists individual part operations in ascending order from raw material to the final product.

Assembly buffer   Construct used to insure that those assembly operations directly fed by the constraint do not wait for material to arrive from non-constrained legs within the net. The assembly buffer also determines the release schedule for raw material into those operations which feed the assembly buffer.

Assembly schedule   A schedule used to sequence the arrival of parts to an assembly operation from non-constraint operations. Assembly schedules are only used when at least one leg of the assembly operation is being fed by the constraint(s).

Backward rods   Rods which require an order to be scheduled across a constraining resource at a given amount of time after a previous order on the same or a different resource.

Batch rods   A time mechanism used to separate/protect orders (batches) on the same resource schedule.

Behavioral constraint   A behavior that is in conflict with reality and blocks the exploitation of a the physical constraint.

Bottleneck   A resource is a bottleneck when the demand placed on a resource is equal to or more than capacity.

Budget   A performance measurement, the budget is used to relate the forecasted expenditure requirements at the department level. This information is used to predict and control operating expense and should not be used to focus improvement.

Buffer   A time mechanism used to protect those portions of the factory (buffer origins) that are vulnerable to problems associated with statistical fluctuations.

Buffer management   A technique used to manage the amount of protection necessary and the process of controlling the buffer origins within the plant.

Buffer management report   The buffer management report consolidates the input of the buffer management worksheet and determines the relative impact by injecting the throughput dollar day and inventory dollar day equation.

Buffer management worksheet Organized to facilitate quantitative analysis and to insure uniformity in data collection, the buffer management worksheet is used by the buffer manager to collect and assemble data relevant to those orders which require being expedited.

Buffer manager The person designated to manage the buffer and insure that the buffer origin is protected by expediting material causing holes in zone I of the buffer.

Buffer origin That portion of the system that needs protection and is the object of the buffer. Buffer origins include, but are not limited to, the constraint, the secondary/tertiary constraint(s), shipping and those assembly operations having one leg being fed by the constraint.

Buffer system The total system used to protect the constraint from the impact of statistical fluctuations.

Buffer zones Refers to the three zones within the buffer management process. (*see also* **Tracking zone** and **Expedite zone**)

Capacity Usually expressed in hours minutes or quantities for a given period of time, capacity is the capability of a resource to react to demand.

Capacity constrained resource (CCR) A resource which has, in aggregate, less capacity than the market demands.

Categories of legitimate reservations Used in the TOC thinking process, the categories of legitimate reservation question the existence of a specific entity, its cause or the relationship between them.

Cause insufficiency Used in the TOC thinking process to define a situation in which the suspected cause is insufficient to explain the result.

CCR (*see* **Capacity constrained resource**)

Combination plants Manufacturing plants which have more than one of the VAT characteristics. (*see also* **V-plant, A-plant** and **T-plant**)

Combination rods Rods which require an order to be scheduled across a constraining resource a given amount of time before and after a previous or succeeding order on the same or a different resource.

Constraint   Anything which limits the system from attaining its goal. Constraints are categorized in the following manner:

- Behavioral
- Managerial
- Capacity
- Market
- Logistical

Constraint buffer   Used to protect the constraint(s) and to determine the release of raw material to those operations which feed the constraint.

Constraint management   The practice of managing resources and organizations in accordance with theory of constraints principles (APICS).

Constraint schedule   The schedule created for a capacity constrained resource in order to exploit its productive capability.

Continuous profit improvement   The five-step process designed to continuously improve the profits of the company. The steps include

- Identifying the constraint
- exploiting the constraint
- Subordinating the non-constraints
- Elevating the constraint
- Repeating the process

Converging operations   Operations which receive parts from more than one part/operation.

Cost mentality   The tendency to optimize local measurements at the expense of global measurements.

Currently reality tree (CRT)   Used to find the core cause or causes from undesirable effects (UDEs).

Dependent setup   Used to maximize the utilization of the constrained resource by combining setups on orders for two different part/operations having the same setup requirement.

Dependent variable environment   The environment where resources are dependent on each other in their capability to produce and are subject to variation in that capability.

Descending part/operations list   A feature of the system which lists individual part/operations in descending order.

Desirable effect   Used in the TOC thinking process in the creation of the future reality tree, identifies those effects which are beneficial and are created as a result of an injection.

Diverging operations   Operations which deliver parts to more than one part/operation.

Drum   The schedule for the primary constraint, establishing the rate at which the system generates throughput.

Drum-buffer-rope   A scheduling technique developed using the theory of constraints. The drum is the schedule for the primary constraint and establishes the rate at which the system generates throughput. The buffer is a time mechanism used to protect those places within the schedule which are particularly vulnerable to disruptions. The rope is the mechanism used to synchronize the factory to the rate of the constraint and determines the release date for material at gating operations

Dynamic buffering   A method used to improve the buffering process so that overall buffer sizes can be shrunk. The buffer is allowed to grow when increases in resource demand require additional lead time. Dynamic buffers shrink as demand declines.

Dynamic data   Data which are allowed to change as the environment and reality change.

Effect-cause-effect   A method formerly used in the TOC thinking process that looked for core causes by continually establishing cause and effect relationships and supporting each relationship with an additional effect.

Elevating the constraint   The act of increasing the ability of the constraint in the creation of throughput by means other than exploitation.

Entity   Used in the TOC thinking process. the entity is used to identify either a cause or an effect.

Entity existence   Used in the TOC thinking process, one of the categories of legitimate reservation which questions the existence of an entity.

Exploitation   The process of increasing the efficiency of the constrained resource without obtaining more of the resource from outside the company. Exploitation may include, but is not limited to, the implementation of statistical process control, total productive maintenance, setup reduction or savings, creating a schedule, and the application of overtime on a constraint resource

Expedite zone   Zone I of the buffer. The expedite zone is used to indicate when the absence of an order is threatening the exploitation of the constraint and to notify the buffer manager when to expedite parts.

Excess capacity   Capacity which is not used to either produce or protect the creation of throughput.

Evaporating clouds (EC)   Used to model the assumptions made which block the creation of a breakthrough solution.

First day peak load   A load placed on a resource during the subordination process which exceeds available capacity on the first day of the planning horizon.

Forward rods   Rods which require an order to be scheduled across a constraining resource a given amount of time prior to a succeeding order on the same or a different resource.

Future reality tree (FRT)   Used to model the changes created after defining breakthrough changes from the evaporating cloud.

Global measurements   Those measurements used to measure effectiveness from outside the company (e.g., return on investment).

Glue   A technique used during setup saving to attach orders together for the purpose of scheduling the constraint. Once orders have been attached they remain attached until the order is complete.

"Haystack compatible" system   A term referring to an information system based on the theory constraints and inspired by *The Haystack Syndrome* by Eli Goldratt.

Holes in the buffer   A phrase which refers to the absence of orders within zones I or II of the protective mechanism called the buffer.

Inertia   The tendency to continue looking at a specific problem or activity the same way even though the situation has changed.

Injection   Used in the TOC thinking process, the injection is the change used to eliminate undesirable effects.

Intermediate objective   In the TOC thinking process, an objective attained to overcome an obstacle defined in the prerequisite.

Inventory   One of the key measurements used to manage a TOC company. It is defined by Eli Goldratt as "all the money the system invests in purchasing things the system intends to sell."

Inventory dollar days   A measurement used to minimize those activities which occur before they are scheduled. It is represented by the formula inventory quantity multiplied by dollar value multiplied by the number of days early.

Leg   A term used when referring to the product flow diagram or net. A leg is a string of part/operations which feed one part to an assembly operation. By definition an assembly operation will have two or more legs.

Leveling the load   A phrase used to describe the initial attempt at scheduling the constraint. The objective is to place each order on the time line so that there are no conflicts between orders and so that it does not exceed daily capacity.

Local measurements   Performance measures used at the department level to guide activity.

Logical implementation   One of the three phases of implementation of the TOC based system, the logical implementation involves changes in the way in which the company is managed.

Logistical constraint   Occurs when the planning and control system prevents the company from attaining its goal.

Managerial constraint   A management policy that prevents or restricts the company from attaining its goal.

Market constraint   Occurs when market demand is less than the capability of the company to produce.

Market segmentation   A strategy for recession proofing and maximizing profit by creating different markets to absorb capacity from the same resource base.

Master production schedule   Used as input in the creation of the net, the master production schedule is the combination of the forecast and sales order requirements. It provides the initial schedule by which the identification process begins to find the primary constraint.

Moving in time   Unlike the low level code used to control the order of processing in material requirements planning, the TOC system uses time. *Moving in time* is a phrase used to describe the procedure used to process orders on the net. As each order is processed it is placed in time beginning with the end of the planning horizon. Once all activities have been planned for a specific date the system moves in time to pick up those requirements of the preceding period. Planning begins at the end of the planning horizon and moves in time toward time zero.

MPS   (*see* **Master production schedule**)

Near constraint   A resource which is loaded to near capacity levels. While it may not limit the amount of throughput that the system can generate, it can have a negative impact on the subordination process and will result in an increase in inventory and operating expense.

Necessary condition   Boundaries placed on a company's departments or individuals, originating either internally or externally, which serve to regulate activity.

Negative branch   Used in the TOC thinking process, the negative branch is the reason why a certain activity cannot or should not be done. Negative branches are normally trimmed so that solutions become more robust.

The net   The combination of all product flow diagrams for all products on the master schedule.

99-to-1 rule   The rule stating that in a dependent variable environment, only 1% of the activity is required to produce 99% of the impact.

Non-constraint   A resource which has more than enough capacity to meet the market demand.

Non-constraint schedule   A schedule produced for non-constraint resources presenting those activities which must not be done prior to a specific time.

Obstacle   Used in the TOC thinking process, the obstacle is defined as something that will negate or reduce the effect of the injection and its impact on the undesirable effect.

Off-loading   The process of removing specific orders from a constraint resource and placing them on a non-constraint resource.

Operating expense   One of the key measurements used to manage a TOC company. It is defined by Eli Goldratt as "all the money the system spends turning inventory into throughput."

Overtime schedule   The schedule for overtime requirements resulting from the exploitation process. The schedule includes the resource on which the overtime is to be spent, the application date and the amount of time required.

Part/operation   A combination of the part number from a bill of material and the operation within a routing that is used to produce a specific part. It represents the smallest element within the product flow diagram.

Peak load   A period in time when the demand placed on a specific resource exceeds capacity.

Permanent education program   An education program designed to support the implementation and execution of the theory of constraints.

Physical implementation   That part of the implementation involving the interface of the user with the system, which includes plant layout, schedule generation, schedule execution and buffer management.

Prerequisite tree (PT)   Used in the TOC thinking process, a flowchart that uncovers and solves intermediate obstacles to achieving goals.

Process batch size   The number of parts processed on a resource without intervening setup.

Process of continuous profit improvement   The five-step process used in the theory of constraints including identification, exploitation, subordination, elevation and repeating the process.

Product flow diagram   A diagram made from the combination of a bill of material and routing for a single product. It presents individual part/operations and their relative positions within the production process.

Productive capacity   That capacity required to produce a given set of products, not including that capacity used to protect the schedule from natural fluctuations in capability.

Protective capacity   That capacity used to protect the capability of a resource or group of resources in meeting the schedule.

Pushing the load   The process of shifting resource load into later periods.

Pushing the order   The act of pushing a specific sales order on the schedule into a later time period.

Raw material schedule   The schedule produced by the system that defines the quantity and date of raw material requirements.

Recession proofing   A methodology designed to ensure that the company will continue to grow regardless of the economic environment in which it exists. Included in the recession proofing process is the ability to

- Continuously implement the five-step process of improvement
- Minimize the impact of a recession by protecting resources through proper market segmentation
- Make valid decisions

Red lane   The string of resources that lead from the primary constraint to the sales order. The red lane is the most vulnerable portion of the factory.

Release schedule   The schedule for the release of raw material into the gating operations.

Reservation   (*see* **Categories of legitimate reservation**)

Road map   (*see* **TOC thinking process**)

Rods   (*see* **Time rods** and **Batch rods**)

Rod violation   Occasion when a specific order having forward, backward or combination rods is compromised by a schedule in which another order occupies space too close in time.

Rope   The rope is the mechanism used to synchronize the factory to the rate of the constraint and determine the release date for material at gating operations.

Schedule conflict   A situation in which part/operations or batches scheduled on a given resource are in conflict with other part/operations or batches due to a lack of adequate protection.

Secondary constraint   A resource whose capacity is limited to the extent that it threatens the subordination of the primary constraint.

Setup savings   The act of combining orders to reduce the number of setups or time spent for setups and thereby increase the amount of protective or productive capacity.

Shop floor control   That activity associated with controlling the production process, including (1) controlling the priority of work (the schedule for the constraints, the release of orders to the gating operations, the schedule for the assembly buffer, the schedule for the shipping buffer, and the buffer management system); (2) collecting and feeding order movement, location and quantity information back to the shop floor control system; and (3) Measurement tracking (collecting and reporting data for maintaining throughput dollar days and inventory dollar days statistics).

Shipping buffer   Used to protect the shipping of finished goods, determine the initial schedule for the constraint and establish the release schedule for raw material which does not go through the constraint or assembly buffer.

Static buffer   That portion of the buffer which is used to protect the buffer origin but is not allowed to fluctuate.

Statistical fluctuation   The result of a law of nature which states that all things will vary and is evidenced in a manufacturing environment by the fluctuation in the ability of a resource to meet a specific schedule.

Static data   Data which are unrelated to the changes which occur in the environment in which it is used.

Station   (*see* **Part/operation**)

Subordination   Providing the constraint what it needs from other resources to maximize the amount throughput generated.

Technical implementation   That portion of the implementation dealing with hardware and software including system selection, integration and testing.

Temporary bottleneck   A situation created when the demand for time on a specific resource temporarily exceeds its capacity.

Tertiary constraint   The third physical constraint identified during the scheduling process.

Theory of constraints (TOC)   A management philosophy developed by Dr. Eliyahu M. Goldratt that can be viewed as three separate but interrelated areas—logistics, performance measurements and logical thinking. Logistics includes drum-buffer-rope scheduling, buffer management, and VAT analysis. Performance measurement includes throughput, inventory and operating expense and the five focusing steps. Thinking process tools are important in identifying the root problem (current reality tree), identifying and expanding win–win solutions (evaporating clouds and future reality tree), and developing implementation plans (prerequisite tree and transition tree) (APICS).

Throughput   One of the key measurements used to manage a TOC company. It is defined by Eli Goldratt as "the rate at which the system generates money through sales."

Throughput accounting   The use of the three basic measurements of throughput, inventory and operating expense to manage the financial/accounting aspects of the company and make decisions.

Throughput chain   A unique chain of resources, processes or products connected by the generation of throughput. (Also referred to as throughput channel.)

Throughput dollar days   A measurement used to minimize those activities which threaten the constraint. It is represented by the formula throughput dollar value multiplied by the number of days late.

Throughput justification   The process of justifying expenditures based on their impact to throughput.

Time line   The time on the planning horizon.

Time rods   A time mechanism used to separate/protect orders (batches) on schedules for different resources.

Time zero   The current date and time.

T-plant   T-plants are characterized by a relatively low number of common raw material and component parts optioned into a large number of end items.

Tracking zone   Zone II of the buffer requiring that orders not having been received at the buffer origin before a specific time be located and tracked for possible problems

Transfer batch size   The number of parts moved from one resource to the next during production.

Transition tree (TT)   Used in the TOC thinking process to define those actions necessary to achieve a goal.

TQM II   The application of the focusing mechanisms and tools of the theory of constraints to the tools and methodologies provided by total quality management.

Undesirable effect (UDE)   Used in the current reality tree of the TOC thinking process, the undesirable effect identifies those effects in the environment which are unwanted.

VAT analysis   The analysis of how resources perform based on the way in which they interface with each other.

V-plant   V-plants are characterized by constantly diverging operations with a small number of raw material items being converted into a large number of end items.

Zone profile   The percentage of on time delivery for zones one and two of the buffer.

Zone I   (*see* **Expedite zone**)

Zone II   (*see* **Tracking zone**)

Zone III   That portion of the buffer which does not include the expedite or tracking zone.

Index

assembly buffer
  origin,
  definition, 112-115
  utilization, 112-115

buffer
  assembly, 112-115
  constraint, 112-115
  dynamic, 115-124
  fixed, 115-116
  Pareto analysis, 149
  shipping, 112-115
  static, 115-116
  variable, 115-124
  zones, 143-144
buffer manager, 150
buffer management, 53, 141-151, 220-222
buffer management report, 148
buffer management worksheet, 147-148
buffer system
  definition, 112-113
  utilization, 112-115

capacity requirements planning, 25-28
cascading effect, 20-21
cash flow management, 181-182
client/server, 237-239

closed-loop system, 2
computer platform, 236-239
conflict between schedules, resolution, 125-130
constraint
  elevation, 4
  exploitation, 52, 82-109
  identification, 61-79
  subordination to, 52, 110-139
constraint buffer, 112-115
current reality tree, 261

data
  definition, 41
  static vs. dynamic
  in shop floor control, 35-36
  in material requirements planning, 17-21
decision-making
  scrap vs. rework, 185-188
  strategic, definition, 153
  support, 152-240
  tactical, definition, 153
demand
  accumulation, 74-75
  aggregation, 9, 15-16
dispatching
  methods of prioritization, 29-31